37

SERIES EXPANSIONS FOR MATHEMATICAL PHYSICISTS

UNIVERSITY MATHEMATICAL TEXTS

1. *Determinants and Matrices* ... ... A. C. Aitken, D.Sc., F.R.S.
2. *Statistical Mathematics* ... ... A. C. Aitken, D.Sc., F.R.S.
3. *Integration* ... ... R. P. Gillespie, Ph.D.
4. *Integration of Ordinary Differential Equations* E. L. Ince, D.Sc.
5. *Vector Methods* ... ... D. E. Rutherford, D.Sc., Dr.Math.
6. *Theory of Equations* ... ... H. W. Turnbull, F.R.S.
7. *Functions of a Complex Variable* ... E. G. Phillips, M.A., M.Sc.
8. *Waves* ... ... C. A. Coulson, M.A., D.Sc., F.R.S.
9. *Infinite Series* ... ... J. M. Hyslop, D.Sc.
10. *Analytical Geometry of Three Dimensions* ... ... W. H. McCrea, Ph.D., F.R.S.
11. *Electricity* ... ... C. A. Coulson, M.A., D.Sc., F.R.S.
12. *Projective Geometry* ... ... T. E. Faulkner, Ph.D.
13. *Introduction to the Theory of Finite Groups* ... ... W. Ledermann, Ph.D., D.Sc.
14. *Classical Mechanics* ... ... D. E. Rutherford, D.Sc., Dr.Math.
15. *Partial Differentiation* ... ... R. P. Gillespie, Ph.D.
16. *Volume and Integral* ... W. W. Rogosinski, Dr.Phil., F.R.S.
17. *Tensor Calculus* ... ... B. Spain, Ph.D.
18. *German-English Mathematical Vocabulary* S. Macintyre, Ph.D., and E. Witte, M.A.
19. *Special Functions of Mathematical Physics and Chemistry* ... ... I. N. Sneddon, D.Sc.
20. *Topology* ... ... E. M. Patterson, Ph.D.
21. *The Theory of Ordinary Differential Equations* ... ... J. C. Burkill, Sc.D., F.R.S.
22. *Fluid Dynamics* ... ... D. E. Rutherford, D.Sc., Dr.Math.
23. *Special Relativity* ... ... W. Rindler, Ph.D.
24. *Real Variable* ... ... J. M. Hyslop, D.Sc.
25. *Russian Reader in Pure and Applied Mathematics* ... ... P. H. Nidditch, Ph.D.
26. *Russian-English Mathematical Vocabulary* J. Burlak, M.Sc., Ph.D., and K. Brooke, M.A.
27. *Introduction to Field Theory* ... Iain T. Adamson, Ph.D.
28. *Number Theory* ... ... J. Hunter, Ph.D.
29. *Numerical Methods:* 1. *Iteration, Programming and Algebraic Equations* ... ... B. Noble, D.Sc
30. *Numerical Methods:* 2. *Differences, Integration and Differential Equations* ... ... B. Noble, D.Sc.
31. *Elementary Abstract Algebra* E. M. Patterson, Ph.D., and D. E. Rutherford, D.Sc., Dr.Math.
32. *Vector Spaces of Finite Dimension* G. C. Shephard, M.A., Ph.D.
33. *Magnetohydrodynamics* ... ... Alan Jeffrey, M.Sc., Ph.D.
34. *An Introduction to Modern Mathematics* ... Albert Monjallon, Agr.de Sc.(Math.)
35. *Quantum Mechanics* ... R. A. Newing, Ph.D., and J. Cunningham, Ph.D.
36. *Probability* ... ... J. R. Gray, B.Sc.
37. *Series Expansions for Mathematical Physicists* ... ... Herbert Meschkowski, Dr.Phil.

SERIES EXPANSIONS FOR MATHEMATICAL PHYSICISTS

HERBERT MESCHKOWSKI

Professor in the Free University of Berlin

Translated by

ROBERT SCHLAPP

Senior Lecturer, Department of Mathematical Physics
University of Edinburgh

OLIVER & BOYD

EDINBURGH AND LONDON

NEW YORK: INTERSCIENCE PUBLISHERS INC.
A DIVISION OF JOHN WILEY & SONS, INC.

OLIVER AND BOYD LTD
Tweeddale Court
Edinburgh 1

39A Welbeck Street
London W.1

This is a translation of
Reihenentwicklungen in der mathematischen Physik,
Hochschultaschenbücher No. 51
published in 1963 by Bibliographisches
Institut, A.G., Mannheim

First English edition 1968

PRINTED IN GREAT BRITAIN BY
THE ABERDEEN UNIVERSITY PRESS

PREFACE

The present work is a sequel to the author's previous book on infinite series (H. Meschkowski, *Unendliche Reihen*, Bibliographisches Institut, Mannheim, 1962). Its main subject is the theory of orthogonal series, which is of fundamental importance for the theoretical physicist. Various practical applications are treated, but on the whole the book is mathematical rather than physical; its aim is to provide a simple introduction to the modern theory of series expansions, which should also be intelligible to readers concerned only with applications.

Our purpose has been to lead up to an understanding of the theory of Hilbert spaces, which plays such an important part in modern theoretical physics. We have had to face the difficulty that the Lebesgue integral is required in connection with the space L^2 of functions quadratically integrable in an interval of the real axis. It has of course not been possible to include a treatment of the Lebesgue integral in the present brief account of series expansions; for this the reader is referred to the relevant literature. It should be added that greater prominence has been given to examples of Hilbert spaces which can be defined without the concept of the Lebesgue integral.

The resulting introduction is intended as a stimulus to further study; the list of references to the literature at the end of the volume serves the same purpose.

I am particularly indebted to Mr. W. Nilson for his loyal help in checking the manuscript.

HERBERT MESCHKOWSKI

Berlin, October 1962

CONTENTS

PAGE

CHAPTER VIII

THE SOLUTION OF LINEAR SYSTEMS

CHAPTER IX

REPRODUCING KERNELS

CHAPTER I

INTERPOLATION SERIES

§ **1.1. Problems of interpolation.** Suppose that in measuring a physical quantity the measured values y_ν ($\nu = 1,2,3,\ldots,n$) correspond to the arguments x_ν ($\nu = 1,2,3,\ldots,n$). In looking for a simple function $y = f(x)$ which associates values $y_\nu = f(x_\nu)$ with the arguments x_ν, it is reasonable to attempt a representation by means of a polynomial of degree $n-1$:

$$y = f(x) = a_0 + a_1x + a_2x^2 + \ldots + a_{n-1}x^{n-1}. \quad (1.1)$$

The coefficients a_μ ($\mu = 0,1,2,\ldots,n-1$) of the polynomial (1.1) can be calculated from the system of equations

$$\begin{aligned} a_0 + a_1x_1 + a_2x_1^2 + \ldots + a_{n-1}x_1^{n-1} &= y_1, \\ a_0 + a_1x_2 + a_2x_2^2 + \ldots + a_{n-1}x_2^{n-1} &= y_2, \\ &\ldots \\ a_0 + a_1x_n + a_2x_n^2 + \ldots + a_{n-1}x_n^{n-1} &= y_n, \end{aligned} \quad (1.2)$$

since the determinant † of this system, namely

$$D = \begin{vmatrix} 1 & x_1 & x_1^2 & \ldots & x_1^{n-1} \\ 1 & x_2 & x_2^2 & \ldots & x_2^{n-1} \\ & & \ldots & & \\ 1 & x_n & x_n^2 & \ldots & x_n^{n-1} \end{vmatrix} = \prod_{\rho<\sigma} (x_\rho - x_\sigma)$$

never vanishes, provided the x_ν are all distinct.

This procedure is, however, somewhat circuitous. A much more convenient way of achieving our object is to write the polynomial (1.1) in the form

$$y = f(x) = A_1 + A_2(x-x_1) + \ldots + A_n(x-x_1)(x-x_2)\ldots(x-x_{n-1}). \quad (1.3)$$

† See, e.g. Aitken, *Determinants and Matrices*, p. 41.

It is easy to calculate the coefficients A_ν of (1.3).

Clearly we have

$$y_1 = f(x_1) = A_1, \qquad y_2 = f(x_2) = y_1 + A_2(x_2 - x_1),$$

so that

$$A_1 = y_1, \qquad A_2 = \frac{y_2 - y_1}{x_2 - x_1},$$

or, in general †

$$A_\nu = A_\nu(x_1, x_2, \dots x_\nu) = \sum_{\mu=1}^{\nu} y_\mu \left[\prod_{m=1}^{\nu}{}' (x_\mu - x_m) \right]^{-1}. \quad (1.4)$$

This can readily be proved by induction. Thus the solution of our problem of interpolation is given by **Newton's interpolation formula**

$$y = f(x) = A_1 + \sum_{\nu=2}^{n} A_\nu (x - x_1)(x - x_2) \dots (x - x_{\nu-1}), \quad (1.5)$$

where the coefficients $A_\nu = A_\nu(x_1, \dots x_\nu)$ are to be calculated by (1.4).

If, conversely, an arbitrary polynomial (1.1) is given, it can always be expressed in Newtonian form by means of (1.5).

These familiar results of classical algebra can immediately be extended to polynomials in the complex plane of $z = x + iy$:

$$w = f(z) = a_0 + a_1 z + \dots + a_{n-1} z^{n-1}. \quad (1.1')$$

We then obtain the Newtonian representation

$$w = f(z) = A_1 + \sum_{\nu=2}^{n} A_\nu (z - z_1)(z - z_2) \dots (z - z_{\nu-1}) \quad (1.5')$$

with coefficients

$$A_\nu = A_\nu(z_1, z_2, \dots z_\nu) = \sum_{\mu=1}^{\nu} w_\mu \left[\prod_{m=1}^{\nu}{}' (z_\mu - z_m) \right]^{-1}. \quad (1.4')$$

It is natural to generalise our problem to infinite sequences x_n or z_n, and correspondingly to analytic functions

† The product sign Π' with an accent means that the factor for which $\mu = m$ is to be omitted.

represented by infinite series. In this way we arrive at the following problems of interpolation.

1. Suppose two (in general complex) sequences z_n and w_n ($n = 1,2,3, \ldots$) to be given, the points z_n lying in a domain **D** of the complex plane. It is required to find a function $w = f(z)$, analytic † in **D**, for which $f(z_n) = w_n$.

2. Suppose two sequences z_n and w_n ($n = 1,2,3, \ldots$) to be given, where the sequence z_n has no limit-point in the finite region of the plane. It is required to find a single-valued function $w = f(z)$ analytic for $|z| < \infty$ (an integral transcendental function), which takes the values w_n at the given points z_n.

3. Suppose a function $w = f(z)$ analytic in a domain **D** of the complex plane to be given, and also a sequence z_n lying wholly within **D**.‡ It is required to find a representation of the function $f(z)$ as an 'interpolating series'

$$f(z) = \sum_{n=0}^{\infty} a_n \phi_n(z), \tag{1.6}$$

where the $\phi_n(z)$ are known functions of z (as simple as possible) and the coefficients a_n are known functions (also as simple as possible) of z_n and $w_n = f(z_n)$:

$$a_n = a_n(z_1, z_2, \ldots, z_n; w_1, w_2, \ldots w_n).$$

4. The corresponding problem can be formulated for integral transcendental functions and sequences z_n which have no limit-point in the finite region of the plane.

We first remark that problem 1 is by no means always soluble. For example, let **D** be the unit disc, $z_n = n^{-1}$, and

$$w_n = \begin{cases} 0 \text{ for odd } n, \\ n^{-1} \text{ for even } n. \end{cases}$$

† A function which is differentiable at all points of a domain **D** of the complex plane is said to be *analytic in* **D**.

‡ The problem may be specialised by the condition that all the limit-points of the sequence z_n should lie in **D**.

The sequences z_n and w_n both converge to 0. Yet there is no function analytic in the neighbourhood of $z = 0$ which takes the values $w_n = f(z_n)$ at the points z_n; for such a function would have to vanish at the points $(2m-1)^{-1}$ $(m = 1,2,3, \ldots)$ and would therefore, by a well-known result in the theory of functions,† vanish identically, so that it could not be equal to $(2m)^{-1}$ for $z = (2m)^{-1}$.

To solve problems 3 and 4, an obvious generalisation of the procedure for polynomials is to make use of series of the form

$$f(z) = A_1 + \sum_{\nu=2}^{\infty} A_\nu(z-z_1)(z-z_2)\ldots(z-z_{\nu-1}). \tag{1.7}$$

If a function $f(z)$ given in **D** can be expressed as a series of the type (1.7) and all the points of interpolation z_n lie in the interior of **D**, the coefficients A_ν can be calculated as in the polynomial representation. In the present case also we have

$$f(z_n) = A_1 + \sum_{\nu=2}^{n} A_\nu(z_n-z_1)\ldots(z_n-z_{\nu-1}).$$

From this we obtain the expression (1.4′) for the A_ν. A special case of the general Newtonian series (1.7), which is of importance in many applications, is obtained by putting $z_n = n$. In this case the series

$$f(z) = A_1 + A_2(z-1) + A_3(z-1)(z-2) + \ldots \tag{1.7'}$$

can be transformed by the substitution

$$A_{\nu+1} = \frac{(-1)^\nu a_\nu}{\nu!}, \qquad (\nu = 0,1,2,\ldots) \tag{1.8}$$

into the form

$$f(z) = \sum_{\nu=0}^{\infty} (-1)^\nu a_\nu \binom{z-1}{\nu}. \tag{1.9}$$

† Copson, *Theory of Functions of a Complex Variable*, p. 74.

§ 1.2. Landau's theorem. To investigate the convergence of a series of the type (1.9), we may compare it with the ' factorial series '

$$g(z) = \sum_{\nu=0}^{\infty} \frac{a_\nu \nu!}{(z)_\nu}, \tag{1.10}$$

where $(z)_\nu$ is defined as

$$(z)_\nu = z(z+1)\ldots(z+\nu), \qquad \nu = 0,1,2,3,\ldots \tag{1.11}$$

The following important theorem, due to Landau, then holds for the two series (1.9) and (1.10):

The series (1.9) *and* (1.10) *converge or diverge together, provided z is non-integral and the set of coefficients a_ν is the same for both.*

In the statement that either both series converge, or both diverge, nothing is implied as regards the limiting values in the case of convergence.

To prove this theorem we apply Du Bois Reymond's test for convergence (sometimes known as Abel's test; cf. Meschkowski (3), III or Ferrar, *Convergence*, p. 67), viz.

The series $\Sigma b_\nu c_\nu$ converges if $\Sigma(c_\nu - c_{\nu+1})$ converges absolutely and Σb_ν converges at least conditionally.

Suppose first that the series

$$\sum_{\nu=0}^{\infty} b_\nu = \sum_{\nu=0}^{\infty} \frac{a_\nu \nu!}{z(z+1)\ldots(z+\nu)} \tag{1.12}$$

converges for a certain complex value of z. We then define the quantity c_ν by

$$\begin{aligned} c_\nu &= (-1)^\nu z(z^2-1)\ldots(z^2-\nu^2)(\nu!)^{-2} \\ &= z\left(1-\frac{z^2}{1^2}\right)\left(1-\frac{z^2}{2^2}\right)\ldots\left(1-\frac{z^2}{\nu^2}\right). \end{aligned}$$

But by the properties of infinite products (Meschkowski (3), IX, or Hyslop, *Infinite Series*, VIII) the product

$$\lim_{\nu\to\infty} c_\nu = z\prod_{\nu=1}^{\infty}\left(1-\frac{z^2}{\nu^2}\right)$$

converges for all complex values of z. More precisely, †

$$\lim_{\nu\to\infty} c_\nu = \frac{\sin \pi z}{\pi}. \tag{1.13}$$

Hence a positive number $M(z)$ exists, depending on z but not on ν, such that $|c_\nu| < M(z)$ for all ν. It follows from this that

$$|c_\nu - c_{\nu+1}| = \left|\frac{z^2 c_\nu}{(\nu+1)^2}\right| < M(z)\frac{|z|^2}{(\nu+1)^2}.$$

The series $\Sigma(c_\nu - c_{\nu+1})$ accordingly converges absolutely. By Du Bois Reymond's test we therefore conclude that

$$\sum_{\nu=0}^{\infty} b_\nu c_\nu = \sum_{\nu=0}^{\infty} (-1)^\nu a_\nu \binom{z-1}{\nu},$$

that is the series (1.9), converges.

Now suppose, conversely, that the series

$$\sum_{\nu=0}^{\infty} b_\nu^* = \sum_{\nu=0}^{\infty} (-1)^\nu a_\nu \binom{z-1}{\nu}.$$

converges; then the sequence

$$c_\nu^* = c_\nu^{-1} = \frac{(-1)^\nu (\nu!)^2}{z(z^2-1)\ldots(z^2-\nu^2)}$$

tends to a limiting value:

$$\lim_{\nu\to\infty} c_\nu^* = \frac{\pi}{\sin \pi z}.$$

Thus for non-integral z a positive number $M^*(z)$ exists such that for all ν,

$$|c_\nu^*| < M^*(z).$$

† The result (1.13) is usually proved for real values of z, but it holds when z is complex, as can readily be shown by means of the theory of functions. We do not use the result (1.13) in our proof; it is sufficient that the infinite products should converge for all z.

But then we have

$$|c^*_{\nu+1}-c^*_\nu| = |c^*_\nu|\frac{|z|^2}{|z^2-(\nu+1)^2|} < \frac{M^*(z)|z|^2}{|z^2-(\nu+1)^2|},$$

so that the series $\Sigma(c^*_\nu - c^*_{\nu+1})$ converges absolutely. On account of the assumed convergence of Σb^*_ν, it follows in this case from Du Bois Reymond's test that the series

$$\sum_{\nu=0}^{\infty} b^*_\nu c^*_\nu = \sum_{\nu=0}^{\infty} b_\nu = \sum_{\nu=0}^{\infty} \frac{a_\nu \nu!}{(z)_\nu}$$

converges.

Let us consider some examples. The factorial series

$$\sum_{\nu=0}^{\infty} \{z(z+1)\ldots(z+\nu)\}^{-1} \tag{1.14}$$

converges for all z other than 0, -1, $-2, \ldots,$ as may readily be shown by the ratio test.† From this it follows, by Landau's theorem which we have just proved, that the Newtonian series

$$\sum_{\nu=0}^{\infty} \frac{(-1)^\nu}{\nu!}\binom{z-1}{\nu} \tag{1.15}$$

converges for all complex values of z.

On the other hand, the series expansion for the so-called Beta function :‡

$$B(z,y) = \sum_{\nu=0}^{\infty} \frac{(-1)^\nu}{y+\nu}\binom{z-1}{\nu} \tag{1.16}$$

diverges, when $y = +1$, for $z = 0$, and also for $z = -1$, as may at once be seen by substitution. The factorial series corresponding to (1.16) is

$$g(z,y) = \sum_{\nu=0}^{\infty} \frac{\nu!}{(y+\nu)z(z+1)\ldots(z+\nu)}. \tag{1.17}$$

† Meschkowski (3), p. 22 or Hyslop, *Infinite series*, p. 43.

‡ For details of this function, see Meschkowski (1) p. 166, or Milne-Thomson, *The Calculus of Finite Differences* (1960), p. 316; earlier editions of this reference contain a misprint—$1/B(x,y)$ for $B(x,y)$.

For real values of $y>0$ and $z>1$ we clearly have

$$\frac{\nu!}{(y+\nu)z(z+1)\dots(z+\nu)} < \frac{1}{\nu(\nu+1)}.$$

Hence in this case the series (1.17), and by Landau's theorem the corresponding Newtonian series (1.16) both converge.

The foregoing example raises the question of the form of the domains in which the Newtonian or factorial series converge. For power series the domain of convergence is always a circle (Meschkowski (3), VII or Hyslop, *Infinite Series*, p. 79) whose radius may have any value, including 0 or ∞.

For series of the type (1.9) or (1.10) the regions of convergence are half-planes † specified by the inequality $\text{Re}(z)<\beta$. The limiting cases $\beta = -\infty$ and $\beta = \infty$ are also possible. In the first case the series converges for all z, in the second it diverges for all z.

It is worth noticing that it is much easier to obtain a general picture of the behaviour of the Newtonian series as regards convergence than it is for series of the type (1.7) or (1.7′), provided the points of interpolation $z_1, z_2, z_3, \dots$ do not lie too close together. This is expressed more precisely in the following theorem.

§ 1.3. Gelfond's theorem. *If* $\Sigma\,|\,z_\nu\,|^{-1}$ *converges for the points of interpolation* z_ν *of the general Newtonian series* (1.7), *and if the series* (1.7) *itself converges for an arbitrary complex number* z_0 ($z_0 \neq z_\nu$, $\nu = 1,2,3,\dots$), *then the series* (1.7) *converges uniformly in any arbitrary circle* $|\,z\,|\leqslant R$.

This implies that in this case the function represented by the series (1.7) is an integral transcendental function.

† To prove this result we require Stirling's general approximation to the Γ-function. We omit the proof, as we do not intend to assume this formula: for details, see Meschkowski (1) p. 71, or Milne-Thomson, *The Calculus of Finite Differences.*

We note first that the conditions of Gelfond's theorem are not satisfied for the particular Newtonian series

$$\sum_{\nu=1}^{\infty}(-1)^{\nu}a_{\nu}\binom{z-1}{\nu},$$

since $\Sigma\,|\,z_{\nu}\,|^{-1}$ diverges for the points of interpolation $z_{\nu}=\nu$ $(\nu=1,2,3,\ldots)$. But if we choose for these points $z_{\nu}=\nu^{1+\delta}$, with δ positive, the theorem to be proved is applicable even when δ is arbitrarily small. In this case the series (1.7) either converges for all z or diverges for all z. It is no longer possible, as in the case of series like (1.7′), for the series to converge in a certain region (a half-plane) and diverge in the complementary region.

Du Bois Reymond's convergence test is once again sufficient to establish Gelfond's result. Let us first write the series (1.7) in the form

$$f(z)=A_1+\sum_{\nu=2}^{\infty}b_{\nu}c_{\nu}(z),$$

where

$$b_{\nu}=A_{\nu}\prod_{\mu=1}^{\nu-1}(z_0-z_{\mu}),\qquad c_{\nu}(z)=\prod_{\mu=1}^{\nu-1}\frac{z-z_{\mu}}{z_0-z_{\mu}},\tag{1.18}$$

and assume that Σb_{ν} converges. To apply Du Bois Reymond's test we have to show that $\Sigma(c_{\nu}(z)-c_{\nu+1}(z))$ converges absolutely.

For this purpose we first choose an integer m so large that for all $\nu>m$,

$$|z_{\nu}|>2|z_0|.\tag{1.19}$$

We also assume $|\,z\,|<R$, where R is to be chosen so large that

$$|z_{\mu}|<R\tag{1.20}$$

for all $\mu<m$; no upper bound is, however, imposed on the radius R.

We now break up the product $c_{\nu}(z)$ as follows:

$$c_{\nu}(z)=\prod_{\mu=1}^{m-1}\frac{z-z_{\mu}}{z_0-z_{\mu}}\prod_{\mu=m}^{\nu-1}\frac{z-z_{\mu}}{z_0-z_{\mu}}=p_1(z)p_2(z),\tag{1.21}$$

and find upper bounds for the factors $p_1(z)$, $p_2(z)$ separately. For the first factor we have, by (1.20),

$$|p_1(z)| < \prod_{\mu=1}^{m-1} \frac{R+|z_\mu|}{|z_0-z_\mu|} < 2^{m-1}R^{m-1}\left[\prod_{\mu=1}^{m-1}|z_0-z_\mu|\right]^{-1}$$
$$= AR^{m-1}, \qquad (1.22)$$

where A is independent of R and v. For the second factor we have

$$|p_2(z)| = \prod_{\mu=m}^{v-1}\left\{\left|1-\frac{z}{z_\mu}\right|\bigg/\left|1-\frac{z_0}{z_\mu}\right|\right\}$$
$$< \prod_{\mu=m}^{v-1}\left\{\left(1+\frac{R}{|z_\mu|}\right)\bigg/\left(1-\left|\frac{z_0}{z_\mu}\right|\right)\right\}. \qquad (1.23)$$

Now $\Sigma\, |z_\mu|^{-1}$ converges, by hypothesis, and therefore † the infinite product

$$U(R) = \prod_{\mu=m}^{\infty}\left\{\left(1+\frac{R}{|z_\mu|}\right)\bigg/\left(1-\left|\frac{z_0}{z_\mu}\right|\right)\right\}$$

also converges. Since the factors of this product are all greater than 1, we have

$$p_2(z) < U(R). \qquad (1.24)$$

It now follows from (1.21), (1.22), (1.23) and (1.24) that

$$|c_v(z)| < AR^{m-1}U(R) = U_1(R).$$

But we have assumed $|z| < R$, so that taking account of (1.19) we have, for $v > m$,

$$|c_{v+1}(z)-c_v(z)| < U_1(R)\left|1-\frac{z-z_v}{z_0-z_v}\right|$$
$$< U_1(R)\frac{R+|z_0|}{|z_v|\,|1-(z_0/z_v)|} < 2U_1(R)\frac{R+|z_0|}{|z_v|}.$$

† Meschkowski (3), IX or Hyslop, *Infinite Series*, p. 94.

Since $\Sigma \mid z_\nu \mid^{-1}$ converges, this ensures that $\Sigma(c_\nu - c_{\nu+1})$ converges absolutely. It follows by Du Bois Reymond's test that

$$\sum_{\nu=2}^{\infty} b_\nu c_\nu(z) = \sum_{\nu=2}^{\infty} A_\nu (z-z_1)\dots(z-z_{\nu-1})$$

converges, which was to be proved.

Consider an example. The points of interpolation for the Newtonian series

$$1+\sum_{\nu=2}^{\infty} \frac{(-1)^{\nu-1}}{(\nu!)^2}(z-1)(z-4)\dots(z-(\nu-1)^2) \quad (1.25)$$

are $z = 1, 4, 9, 16, \dots.$ Since $\Sigma \nu^{-2} < \infty$, the conditions of Gelfond's theorem are satisfied. For $z_0 = 0$ (1.25) reduces to

$$1+\sum_{\nu=2}^{\infty} \frac{1}{\nu^2}.$$

Since this series converges, (1.25) converges for all z.

§ **1.4. Interpolation in the unit circle.** So far we have been concerned only with problems of interpolation in which the sequence z_n of points of interpolation has no finite limit-point. The functions appearing as solutions were then non-regular at infinity, that is, at the limit-point of the sequence z_n.

But we may also ask if solutions of the interpolation problem exist which are regular even at the limit-point (or points) of the sequence z_n.

We confine ourselves to the simplest case. Let z_n be a given sequence of points converging to 0. It is required to find a one-valued function, regular in the neighbourhood of $z = 0$, which takes prescribed values w_n at the prescribed points z_n. We have already mentioned that this problem is not always soluble.

Here again the obvious way is to attempt a solution (supposing one to exist) by means of a Newtonian series (1.7), calculating the coefficients by (1.4′). If the resulting series converges, it represents a solution of the interpolation problem.

The question of convergence is particularly simple to decide when the points of interpolation satisfy the condition

$$\overline{\lim_{n\to\infty}}\left|\frac{z_{n+1}}{z_n}\right| = q<1. \tag{1.26}$$

For in this case the behaviour of the series

$$f(z) = A_1 + \sum_{\nu=2}^{\infty} A_\nu(z-z_1)\dots(z-z_{\nu-1}) \tag{1.27}$$

can be compared with that of the 'associated' power series

$$g(z) = \sum_{\nu=1}^{\infty} A_\nu z^\nu . \tag{1.28}$$

If condition (1.26) *is satisfied for the null sequence* z_n *of points of interpolation, the behaviour of the two series* (1.27) *and* (1.28) *as regards convergence is the same.*

It is known † that the series (1.28) has a circle of convergence of radius

$$R = \{\overline{\lim}\,|A_n|^{1/n}\}^{-1}.$$

Hence the corresponding result holds, provided (1.26) is satisfied, for the Newtonian series (1.27).

To prove the above result we first assume that the series (1.28) converges, and define

$$b_\nu = A_\nu z^\nu,$$

$$c_\nu = (z-z_1)(z-z_2)\dots(z-z_{\nu-1})z^{-\nu}, \quad \nu = 2,3,4\dots$$

Then the series Σb_ν converges, and for $\Sigma(c_\nu - c_{\nu+1})$ we have

$$|c_{\nu+1}-c_\nu| = |c_\nu z_\nu z^{-1}|,$$

† Meschkowski (3), VII or Hyslop, *Infinite Series*, p. 79.

and hence

$$\overline{\lim}\left|\frac{c_{\nu+2}-c_{\nu+1}}{c_{\nu+1}-c_\nu}\right| = \overline{\lim}\left|\frac{c_{\nu+1}z_{\nu+1}}{c_\nu z_\nu}\right| = \overline{\lim}\left|\frac{z_{\nu+1}}{z_\nu}\right|\left|1-\frac{z_\nu}{z}\right|$$
$$= q < 1.$$

Thus $\Sigma(c_\nu - c_{\nu+1})$ converges absolutely, and hence the convergence of

$$\sum_{\nu=2}^{\infty} b_\nu c_\nu = \sum_{\nu=2}^{\infty} A_\nu(z-z_1)\ldots(z-z_{\nu-1})$$

follows by Du Bois Reymond's test.

If, conversely, we assume the convergence of (1.27), we can construct a corresponding proof of the convergence of (1.28), using the sequences

$$b_\nu^* = A_\nu(z-z_1)\ldots(z-z_{\nu-1}),$$
$$c_\nu^* = \frac{z^\nu}{(z-z_1)\ldots(z-z_{\nu-1})}.$$

Our results on the convergence of the Newtonian series enable us to solve the interpolation problems 1 and 2 mentioned in § 1.1 by means of such series, at least in those cases in which the sequences z_ν and $w_\nu = f(z_\nu)$ satisfy certain conditions.

To solve the interpolation problems 3 and 4 (p. 3) it is necessary to examine the convergence of the 'remainder' term

$$R_n(z) = (z-z_1)(z-z_2)\ldots$$
$$(z-z_n)\frac{1}{2\pi i}\int\frac{f(t)dt}{(t-z_1)\ldots(t-z_n)(t-z)},$$

where the integral is taken over the boundary of the domain **D**. The more detailed examination of the problems arising in this connection must perforce be omitted.†

† See, e.g. Meschkowski (1), Nörlund, *Differenzenrechnung*, or Milne-Thomson, *The Calculus of Finite Differences*. These works treat the solution of interpolation problems using Newtonian series. For the solution of interpolation problems using certain complete orthonormal systems in Hilbert space see Meschkowski (2).

§ 1.5. Exercises

1. Prove the formula, due to Stirling,

$$\frac{1}{z}-\frac{1}{z+h}=\sum_{n=0}^{\infty}\frac{(h)_n}{(z+h)_{n+1}}.$$

2. Investigate the convergence of

(a) $$\sum_{n=0}^{\infty}\frac{\rho^n}{z(z+1)\dots(z+n)}, \qquad |\rho|<1.$$

(b) $$\sum_{n=0}^{\infty}y^n\binom{z-1}{n}, \qquad |y|<1.$$

(c) $$\sum_{n=1}^{\infty}z(z-\tfrac{1}{2})(z-\tfrac{1}{4})\dots(z-\tfrac{1}{2^n}).$$

3. Show that the series

$$g(z)=\sum_{n=0}^{\infty}\frac{(-1)^n}{z+n}$$

satisfies the difference equation

$$g(z+1)+g(z)=z^{-1}.$$

4. Transform the integral

$$J(z)=\int_0^{\infty}\left(\frac{e^{-t}}{1-e^{-t}}-\frac{e^{-zt}}{1-e^{-t}}\right)dt$$

into a Newtonian series with z as variable.

CHAPTER II

TRIGONOMETRIC SERIES

§ **2.1. The problem.** Many physical processes are of a periodic character. They can be described by functions satisfying a functional relation of the form (see Fig. 1):

$$f(x+\lambda) = f(x). \tag{2.1}$$

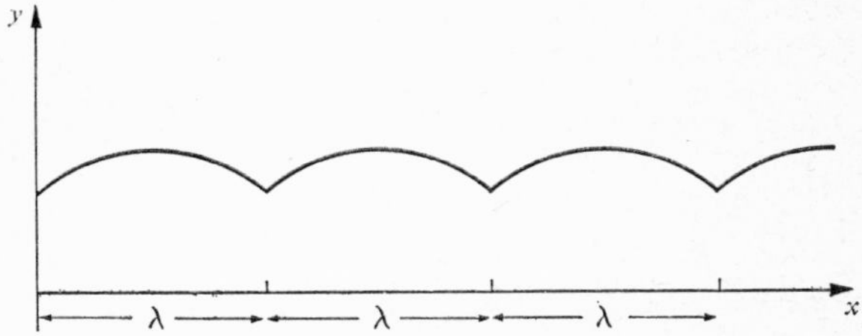

Fig. 1.

A particularly simple example of such a periodic function (of period 2π) is the function $y = \sin x$. It can be used, for example, to represent the time-dependence of the current strength J of an alternating current (Fig. 2 for $\nu = 1$):

$$J = a \sin 2\pi\nu t. \tag{2.2}$$

We now enquire how other periodic functions (e.g. like that shown in Fig. 1) may be represented analytically by means of known periodic functions. For simplicity, let us confine ourselves at first to functions of period $\lambda = 2\pi$. In this case an approximation by sums of the form †

$$g_n(x) = \tfrac{1}{2}A_0 + \sum_{\nu=1}^{n} (A_\nu \cos \nu x + B_\nu \sin \nu x) \tag{2.3}$$

† It is convenient, as will appear later, to denote the constant term by $\tfrac{1}{2}A_0$ rather than A_0.

suggests itself. For all integral ν we have

$$\cos \nu(x+2\pi) = \cos \nu x, \quad \sin \nu(x+2\pi) = \sin \nu x,$$

so that for the function $g_n(x)$ represented by (2.3) we also have

$$g_n(x+2\pi) = g_n(x). \tag{2.4}$$

We could now try to approximate a periodic function $f(x)$ of period 2π by a sum $g_n(x)$ in such a way as to make $|f(x)-g_n(x)|$ as small as possible. The function is said to

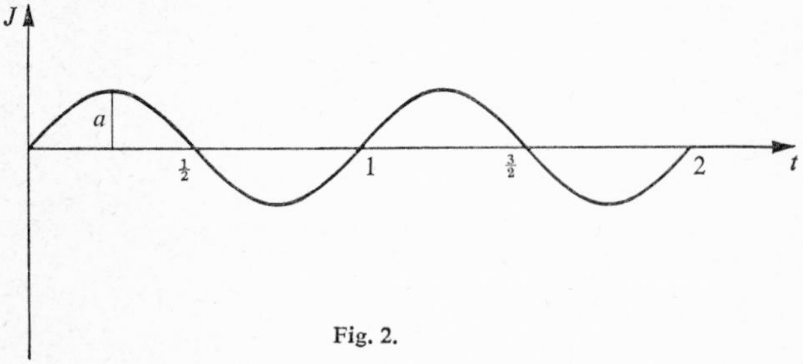

Fig. 2.

be approximated **uniformly** by trigonometric sums (2.3) if for all $\varepsilon > 0$ there exists a sum $g_n(x)$ such that

$$|f(x)-g_n(x)| < \varepsilon$$

for all x.

This uniform approximation is to be clearly distinguished from **approximation in mean.** In the latter case the 'mean square error'

$$J = \int_{-\pi}^{\pi} \{f(x)-g_n(x)\}^2 dx \tag{2.5}$$

is to be made as small as possible.

Consider the following problem: Given a sectionally continuous † function $f(x)$ of period 2π, determine the

† A function is said to be *sectionally continuous* in an interval if it is continuous in the interval except at a finite number of discontinuities.

coefficients A_ν and B_ν ($\nu = 0,1,2, \ldots, n$; $B_0 = 0$) so as to make (2.5) a minimum. This problem is easily solved if we take account of the **orthogonal property** of the functions $\sin \nu x$ and $\cos \nu x$, according to which the relations

$$\frac{1}{\pi}\int_{-\pi}^{\pi} \sin \nu x \sin \mu x dx = \frac{1}{\pi}\int_{-\pi}^{\pi} \cos \nu x \cos \mu x dx = \delta_{\nu\mu}, \tag{2.6}$$

$$\frac{1}{\pi}\int_{-\pi}^{\pi} \sin \nu x \cos \mu x dx = 0 \tag{2.6'}$$

hold for all integral ν, μ, where $\delta_{\nu\mu}$ is the well-known **Kronecker symbol:**

$$\delta_{\nu\mu} = \begin{cases} 0 \text{ for } \nu \neq \mu, \\ 1 \text{ for } \nu = \mu. \end{cases}$$

The properties (2.6) and (2.6′) are readily proved by transforming the integrands by the addition theorem. For example,

$$\sin \nu x \sin \mu x = \tfrac{1}{2}\{\cos (\nu-\mu)x - \cos (\nu+\mu)x\}.$$

For convenience in evaluating the integral (2.5) we introduce the following notation:

$$\begin{aligned} a_\nu &= \frac{1}{\pi}\int_{-\pi}^{\pi} f(x) \cos \nu x dx, \\ b_\nu &= \frac{1}{\pi}\int_{-\pi}^{\pi} f(x) \sin \nu x dx, \qquad \nu = 0,1,2, \ldots n. \end{aligned} \tag{2.7}$$

Then using (2.6) and (2.6′) we have

$$\begin{aligned} \frac{1}{\pi}J &= \frac{1}{\pi}\int_{-\pi}^{\pi} \left\{f(x) - \tfrac{1}{2}A_0 - \sum_{\nu=1}^{n} (A_\nu \cos \nu x + B_\nu \sin \nu x)\right\}^2 dx \\ &= \frac{1}{\pi}\int_{-\pi}^{\pi} f^2 dx + \tfrac{1}{2}A_0^2 + \sum_{\nu=1}^{n} (A_\nu^2 + B_\nu^2) - \\ &\qquad\qquad 2\sum_{\nu=1}^{n} (a_\nu A_\nu + b_\nu B_\nu) - a_0 A_0, \end{aligned}$$

or

$$\frac{1}{\pi}J = \frac{1}{\pi}\int_{-\pi}^{\pi} f^2 dx - \sum_{\nu=1}^{n} a_\nu^2 - \sum_{\nu=1}^{n} b_\nu^2 - \tfrac{1}{2}a_0^2 + \sum_{\nu=1}^{n} (a_\nu - A_\nu)^2 +$$

$$\sum_{\nu=1}^{n} (b_\nu - B_\nu)^2 + \tfrac{1}{2}(a_0 - A_0)^2. \qquad (2.8)$$

The coefficients a_ν and b_ν are determined by the given function $f(x)$ in accordance with (2.7). We now choose the coefficients A_ν and B_ν so as to make J as small as possible. Clearly this can be done by making the last three non-negative terms vanish. So we put

$$A_\nu = a_\nu, \qquad B_\nu = b_\nu, \qquad \nu = 0,1,2,3, \ldots, n. \qquad (2.9)$$

This means that of all the trigonometric sums (2.3), the one that is the best approximation in mean to the given function is

$$\tfrac{1}{2}a_0 + \sum_{\nu=1}^{n} (a_\nu \cos \nu x + b_\nu \sin \nu x),$$

where the coefficients a_ν and b_ν are determined by the integrals (2.7). They are known as the **Fourier coefficients** of the function $f(x)$.

Let us consider an example. Suppose $f_1(x)$ is the periodic function of period 2π defined in the interval $[-\pi,\pi]$ by the equation $f_1(x) = |x|$. Fig. 3 shows the graph of this function.

In this case, using the relations

$$|x| \cos \nu x = |-x| \cos(-\nu x),$$

and

$$|-x| \sin(-\nu x) = -|x| \sin \nu x,$$

we obtain for the integrals (2.7),

$$a_\nu = \frac{1}{\pi}\int_{-\pi}^{\pi} |x| \cos \nu x dx = \frac{2}{\pi}\int_{0}^{\pi} x \cos \nu x dx, \qquad b_\nu = 0. \quad (2.10)$$

It follows from this, by integration by parts, that

$$a_0 = \pi, \quad a_{2\nu} = 0 \text{ for } \nu \geqslant 1, \quad a_{2\nu+1} = -\frac{4}{\pi(2\nu-1)^2}. \tag{2.11}$$

Thus the trigonometric sum

$$S_{2n-1}(x) = \frac{\pi}{2} - \frac{4}{\pi}\left(\cos x + \frac{\cos 3x}{3^2} + \ldots + \frac{\cos(2n-1)x}{(2n+1)^2}\right)$$

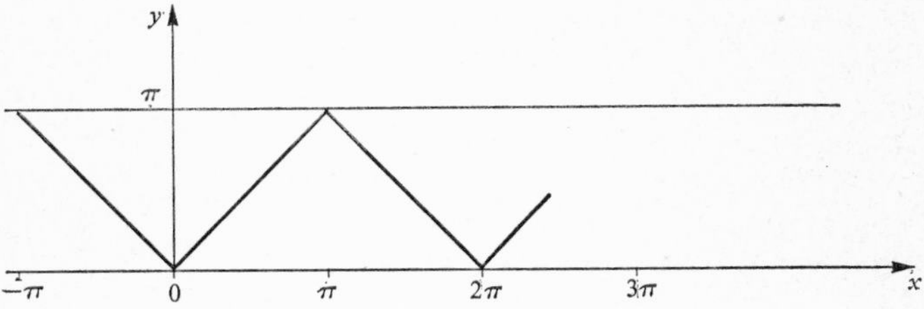

Fig. 3.

is a better approximation in mean to the function $f_1(x)$, represented by the graph of Fig. 3, than any other sum

$$\sigma_{2n-1}(x) = \tfrac{1}{2}A_0 + \sum_{\nu=1}^{2n-1} (A_\nu \cos \nu x + B_\nu \sin \nu x).$$

In Fig. 4 the graph of the function $f_1(x)$ is again shown (in the interval $[-\pi, \pi]$), along with those of the approximating sums S_3 and S_7.

If we put $A_\nu = a_\nu$, $B_\nu = b_\nu$ in equation (2.8) and note that $J \geqslant 0$, we obtain the inequality

$$\tfrac{1}{2}a_0^2 + \sum_{\nu=1}^{n} (a_\nu^2 + b_\nu^2) \leqslant \frac{1}{\pi}\int_{-\pi}^{\pi} f^2 dx. \tag{2.12}$$

Since this inequality—known as **Bessel's inequality**—holds for all integral n, we have the following important theorem:

The sum of the squares of the Fourier coefficients of a sectionally continuous function converges:

$$\tfrac{1}{2}a_0^2+\sum_{\nu=1}^{\infty}(a_\nu^2+b_\nu^2)<\infty, \tag{2.13}$$

where a_ν and b_ν are the integrals given by (2.7).

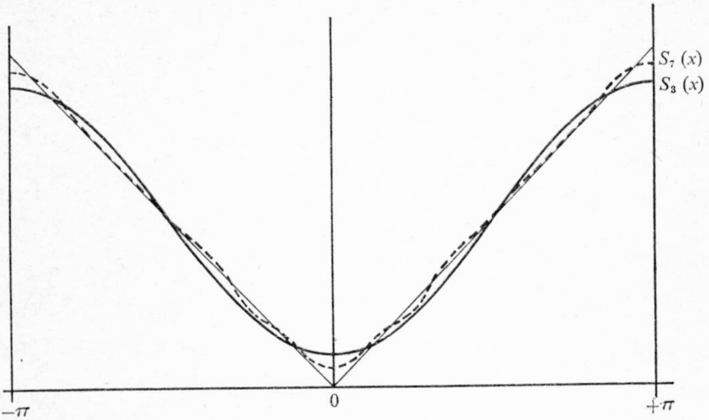

Fig. 4.

§ 2.2. Definition of Fourier series. An obvious step would be to replace the approximation to a periodic function of period 2π by a series representation

$$f(x)=\tfrac{1}{2}a_0+\sum_{\nu=1}^{\infty}(a_\nu\cos\nu x+b_\nu\sin\nu x). \tag{2.14}$$

Series of the type (2.14) are known as **trigonometric series** or **Fourier series.**

If a sectionally continuous function $f(x)$ can be represented by a **uniformly convergent** series (2.14), the coefficients a_ν and b_ν are certainly given by the integrals (2.7). For, if the convergence is uniform, the integrals

$$\int_{-\pi}^{\pi}f(x)\cos\nu x\,dx,\qquad \int_{-\pi}^{\pi}f(x)\sin\nu x\,dx$$

may be evaluated by term-by-term integration (Meschkowski (3) VI or Hyslop *Infinite Series*, p. 75.) which by (2.6) and (2.6′) at once gives formula (2.7) for the coefficients.

A function is said to be **even** in the interval $[-a, a]$ if it satisfies the functional equation $f(-x) = f(x)$ $(x \in [-a, a])$; it is said to be **odd** if $f(-x) = -f(x)$. Examples of even functions (for any interval $[-a, a]$) are

$$\cos x, \qquad x^2, \qquad x^4, \qquad \cosh x, \qquad |x|.$$

Examples of odd functions are

$$\sin x, \qquad \sinh x, \qquad x^3, \qquad x^7;$$

on the other hand the functions

$$e^x, \qquad x^2-4x+5$$

are neither odd nor even.

From the relation (2.7) it is immediately obvious that for any even function $f(x)$ † the coefficients b_ν vanish, while the a_ν are given by

$$a_\nu = \frac{2}{\pi}\int_0^\pi f(x) \cos \nu x dx, \qquad \nu = 0,1,2, \ldots \qquad (2.15)$$

For any odd function the coefficients a_ν vanish, while the b_ν are given by

$$b_\nu = \frac{2}{\pi}\int_0^\pi f(x) \sin \nu x dx, \qquad \nu = 1,2,3, \ldots \qquad (2.15')$$

We may *formally* associate a Fourier series with any sectionally continuous periodic function of period 2π, the coefficients a_ν and b_ν of which are found from (2.7) (or from (2.15) or (2.15′) for even and odd functions respectively). We know that the sum of the squares of the coefficients

† Cf. the case $f_1(x) = |x|$.

always converges (cf. (2.13)). But this is not to say that the series

$$\tfrac{1}{2}a_0+\sum_{\nu=1}^{\infty}(a_\nu \cos \nu x+b_\nu \sin \nu x)$$

itself converges *and also* represents the given function $f(x)$. In the meantime we shall write

$$f(x)\sim\tfrac{1}{2}a_0+\sum_{\nu=1}^{\infty}(a_\nu \cos \nu x+b_\nu \sin \nu x) \qquad (2.16)$$

to denote the formal correspondence of function and series, the coefficients a_ν and b_ν being found from (2.7). The correspondence (2.16) asserts nothing about the convergence or divergence of the formally constructed series. For the example $f_1(x) = |x|$ considered in § 2.1 we have

$$f_1(x)\sim\frac{\pi}{2}-\frac{4}{\pi}\sum_{n=1}^{\infty}\frac{\cos(2n-1)x}{(2n-1)^2}. \qquad (2.17)$$

For the odd function

$$f_2(x)=\begin{cases}+1 \text{ for } (2n\pi,(2n+1)\pi),\\ -1 \text{ for } ((2n+1)\pi,(2n+2)\pi),\\ \quad 0 \text{ for } n\pi,\ n=0,\pm1,\pm2,\ldots\end{cases}$$

calculation of the Fourier coefficients gives the formal correspondence

$$f_2(x)\sim\frac{4}{\pi}\left(\frac{\sin x}{1}+\frac{\sin 3x}{3}+\frac{\sin 5x}{5}+\ldots\right). \qquad (2.18)$$

§ 2.3. A Dirichlet series. For the purpose of later proofs we require the series, constructed formally without regard to convergence, which was first investigated by Dirichlet,

$$D(x)=\sin x+\tfrac{1}{2}\sin 2x+\tfrac{1}{3}\sin 3x+\ldots, \qquad (2.19)$$

whose partial sums are

$$u_n(x)=\sum_{\nu=1}^{n}\frac{1}{\nu}\sin \nu x.$$

To establish the convergence of this series, we first form the derivative of the partial sums:

$$u_n'(x) = \cos x + \cos 2x + \ldots + \cos nx. \qquad (2.20)$$

We write this sum (2.20) in the form

$$\sum_{\nu=1}^{n} \cos \nu x = \frac{1}{2 \sin \frac{1}{2}x} \sum_{\nu=1}^{n} 2 \sin \tfrac{1}{2}x \cos \nu x$$

and transform it, using the result

$$\sin \alpha - \sin \beta = 2 \sin \tfrac{1}{2}(\alpha-\beta) \cos \tfrac{1}{2}(\alpha+\beta),$$

into

$$\sum_{\nu=1}^{n} \cos \nu x = \frac{1}{2 \sin \frac{1}{2}x} \sum_{\nu=1}^{n} (\sin \tfrac{1}{2}(2\nu+1)x - \sin \tfrac{1}{2}(2\nu-1)x)$$

$$= \frac{1}{2 \sin \frac{1}{2}x} (\sin \tfrac{1}{2}(2n+1)x - \sin \tfrac{1}{2}x).$$

It follows from this that

$$u_n(x) = \frac{\sin \frac{1}{2}(2n+1)x}{2 \sin \frac{1}{2}x} - \frac{1}{2}. \qquad (2.21)$$

Consider now the function $U_n(x)$ defined by

$$U_n(x) = u_n(x) + \tfrac{1}{2}x + \frac{1}{2n+1} \cos \tfrac{1}{2}(2n+1)x (\sin \tfrac{1}{2}x)^{-1}. \qquad (2.22)$$

Taking account of (2.21) we find, for the derivative of this function,

$$| U_n'(x) | = -\frac{\cos \frac{1}{2}x \cos \frac{1}{2}(2n+1)x}{2(2n+1) \sin^2 \frac{1}{2}x}. \qquad (2.23)$$

Now let $[a, b]$ be a chosen fixed sub-interval of the open interval $(0, 2\pi)$, i.e. $0<a<b<2\pi$. For this interval we have, by (2.23),

$$U_n'(x) \leqslant \frac{1}{2(2n+1)m},$$

where

$$m = \min(\sin^2 \tfrac{1}{2}a; \sin^2 \tfrac{1}{2}b).$$

It follows from this inequality that $U_n'(x)$ converges uniformly to zero. By well-known results on series † we therefore have, if $a \leqslant \alpha \leqslant \xi \leqslant b$,

$$\lim_{n\to\infty} \int_\alpha^\xi U_n'(x)dx = \int_\alpha^\xi \lim_{n\to\infty} U_n'(x)dx.$$

Hence

$$\lim_{n\to\infty} U_n(x) = \lim_{n\to\infty} \{u_n(x) + \tfrac{1}{2}x + r_n(x)\} = c$$

or

$$D(x) = \lim_{n\to\infty} u_n(x) = -\tfrac{1}{2}x + c - \lim_{n\to\infty} r_n(x), \qquad (2.24)$$

where c is a constant, as yet unknown, and $r_n(x)$ denotes (cf. (2.22))

$$\frac{1}{2n+1} \cos \tfrac{1}{2}(2n+1)x \,(\sin \tfrac{1}{2}x)^{-1}.$$

Clearly $r_n(x)$ also converges uniformly to zero in $[a, b]$. Hence (2.24) gives

$$\lim_{n\to\infty} u_n(x) = -\tfrac{1}{2}x + c$$

or

$$D(x) = -\tfrac{1}{2}x + c = \sin x + \tfrac{1}{2}\sin 2x + \tfrac{1}{3}\sin 3x + \ldots$$

The convergence of this series is *uniform* in any interval not containing 0 or $\pm 2\pi n$ ($n = 1, 2, \ldots$). To determine c we put $x = \frac{1}{2}\pi$; we then obtain (cf. Meschkowski (3) p. 75 or Hyslop, *Infinite Series*, p. 81).

$$D(\tfrac{1}{2}\pi) = 1 - \tfrac{1}{3} + \tfrac{1}{5} - \tfrac{1}{7} + \ldots = \tfrac{1}{4}\pi.$$

Accordingly,

$$\tfrac{1}{2}(\pi - x) = \sin x + \tfrac{1}{2}\sin 2x + \tfrac{1}{3}\sin 3x + \ldots \qquad (2.25)$$

† See, e.g. Meschkowski (3) or Hyslop, *Infinite Series*, p. 75.

for $0<x<2\pi$. Hence the series introduced in (2.19) represents a function $D(x)$ which is given in the open interval $(0, 2\pi)$ by $\frac{1}{2}(\pi-x)$. Because of the periodicity of the terms of (2.25) the values for any other real value $x \mp 2\pi n$ $(n = 0, \pm 1, \pm 2, \ldots)$ follow from the functional equation

$$D(x+2\pi n) = D(x).$$

Finally, if $x = 2\pi n$, we obtain from the series expansion

$$D(x) = \sin x + \tfrac{1}{2}\sin 2x + \tfrac{1}{3}\sin 3x + \ldots \qquad (2.25')$$

the result that $D(2\pi n) = 0$. The graph of this function, which is discontinuous at $x = 2\pi n$, is shown in Fig. 5.

A function $f(x)$ is said to have a **saltus** of amount $\sigma(a)$ at the point a if for every *positive* null sequence h_n

$$\lim_{n\to\infty} f(a+h_n) = f(a^+), \qquad \lim_{n\to\infty} f(a-h_n) = f(a^-)$$

both exist and $f(a^+)-f(a^-) = \sigma(a)$. The values of the function $f(x)$ at the point a can be defined as $f(a^+)$, $f(a^-)$ *or as any other number*. At a point b at which the function is continuous we of course have $f(b) = f(b^+) = f(b^-)$, $\sigma(b) = 0$.

For our function $D(x)$ given by the Dirichlet series (2.25′) we have

$$D(2\pi n) = 0, \quad D(2\pi n^+) = \tfrac{1}{2}\pi, \quad D(2\pi n^-) = -\tfrac{1}{2}\pi, \quad \sigma(2\pi n) = \pi.$$

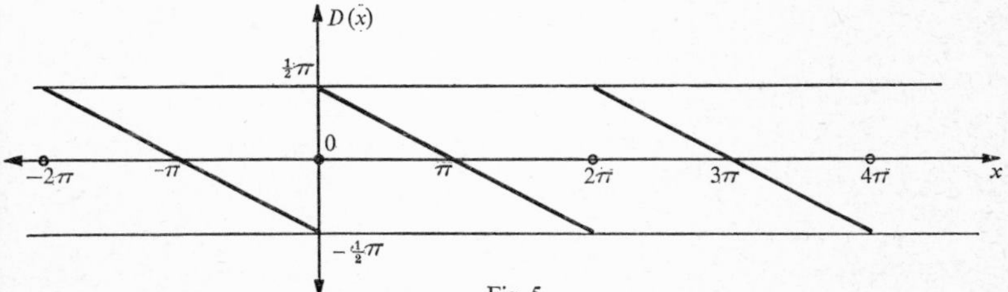

Fig. 5.

Hence

$$D(x) = \tfrac{1}{2}\{D(x^+)+D(x^-)\} \tag{2.26}$$

for all† real x.

§ 2.4. The convergence of the Fourier series of sectionally smooth functions. A function $f(x)$ is said to be **sectionally smooth** in an interval $[a, b]$ of the real axis if it and its first derivative are continuous except for a finite number of points of discontinuity.

We shall now show that:

Every sectionally smooth function of period 2π can be expanded as a Fourier series which converges absolutely and uniformly in every closed interval in which the function is continuous.

To prove this, we first observe that because of the periodicity of $f(x)$ and $f'(x)$, $\cos \nu x$ and $\sin \nu x$, the Fourier coefficients of the given function, and also those of its derivative,

$$\alpha_\nu = \frac{1}{\pi}\int_{-\pi}^{\pi} f'(x) \cos \nu x dx, \quad \beta_\nu = \frac{1}{\pi}\int_{-\pi}^{\pi} f'(x) \sin \nu x dx \tag{2.27}$$

can alternatively be represented by the integrals

$$\alpha_\nu = \frac{1}{\pi}\int_{r}^{r+2\pi} f'(x) \cos \nu x dx, \quad \beta_\nu = \frac{1}{\pi}\int_{r}^{r+2\pi} f'(x) \sin \nu x dx,$$

where r is an arbitrary real number. We now choose r to correspond to a value of x for which $f(x)$ and $f'(x)$ are continuous. Then (2.27) gives, by integration by parts,

$$\alpha_\nu = \frac{1}{\pi}[f(x) \cos \nu x]_r^{r+2\pi} + \frac{1}{\pi}\int_{r}^{r+2\pi} f(x)\nu \sin \nu x dx = \nu b_\nu$$

† Since at points where the function is continuous $D(x^+) = D(x^-) = D(x)$.

and similarly

$$\beta_\nu = 0 - \frac{1}{\pi}\int_r^{r+2\pi} f(x)\nu \cos \nu x dx = -\nu a_\nu,$$

where a_ν and b_ν are the Fourier coefficients of $f(x)$. Thus we have

$$\sum_{\nu=n}^{N} |a_\nu \cos \nu x + b_\nu \sin \nu x| = \sum_{\nu=n}^{N} \frac{1}{\nu} |\alpha_\nu \sin \nu x - \beta_\nu \cos \nu x|. \tag{2.28}$$

We now apply Schwarz's inequality for finite sums † and also the fact that $\alpha_\nu^2 + \beta_\nu^2$ is the maximum value ‡ of $(\alpha_\nu \sin \nu x - \beta_\nu \cos \nu x)^2$. In this way (2.28) gives

$$\left\{\sum_{\nu=n}^{N} |a_\nu \cos \nu x + b_\nu \sin \nu x|\right\}^2$$

$$\leqslant \left(\sum_{\nu=n}^{N} \frac{1}{\nu^2}\right) \sum_{\nu=n}^{N} |\alpha_\nu \sin \nu x - \beta_\nu \cos \nu x|^2 \tag{2.29}$$

$$\leqslant \left(\sum_{\nu=n}^{N} \frac{1}{\nu^2}\right) \sum_{\nu=n}^{N} (\alpha_\nu^2 + \beta_\nu^2)$$

By Bessel's inequality (2.12) applied to the function $f'(x)$,

$$\tfrac{1}{2}\alpha_0^2 + \sum_{\nu=1}^{\infty} (\alpha_\nu^2 + \beta_\nu^2) \leqslant \frac{1}{\pi}\int_{-\pi}^{\pi} f'^2 dx = M^2,$$

and it therefore follows from (2.29) that

$$\sum_{\nu=n}^{N} |a_\nu \cos \nu x + b_\nu \sin \nu x| \leqslant M \sqrt{\left\{\sum_{\nu=n}^{N} \frac{1}{\nu^2}\right\}}. \tag{2.30}$$

† $\left(\sum_{\nu=1}^{n} x_\nu y_\nu\right)^2 \leqslant \sum_{\nu=1}^{n} x_\nu^2 \sum_{\nu=1}^{n} y_\nu^2$. See, e.g., § 5.4.

‡ This can be shown by the methods of differential calculus.

But since $\Sigma\nu^{-2}$ converges,† (2.30) shows that

$$\tfrac{1}{2}a_0+\sum_{\nu=1}^{\infty}(a_\nu \cos \nu x+b_\nu \sin \nu x)$$

converges absolutely and uniformly.

This does not of course necessarily mean that the sum $\phi(x)$ also *represents* the function $f(x)$. Meanwhile, then, let us write

$$f(x)\sim\tfrac{1}{2}a_0+\sum_{\nu=1}^{\infty}(a_\nu \cos \nu x+b_\nu \sin \nu x)=\phi(x). \quad (2.31)$$

§ **2.5. The representation of sectionally smooth functions.** We shall now show that at all points of continuity the functions $f(x)$ and $\phi(x)$ in (2.31) coincide. We first show that, *if the Fourier series of a continuous function converges uniformly, it represents the function.*

Let us therefore suppose that the periodic function $g(x)$ ($g(x+2\pi)=g(x)$) is continuous, though not necessarily smooth, for all real values of x. There is then no saltus at the boundary of the interval $[-\pi,\pi]$, and we have $g(-\pi)=g(\pi)$. Suppose that the Fourier series of $g(x)$,

$$g(x)\sim\tfrac{1}{2}a_0+\sum_{\nu=1}^{\infty}(a_\nu \cos \nu x+b_\nu \sin \nu x)=s(x)$$

converges uniformly in the interval $[-\pi,\pi]$; then the limiting function $s(x)$ of this series is likewise continuous ‡ and the function $h(x)=s(x)-g(x)$ would be a continuous function, all of whose Fourier coefficients vanish:

$$\frac{1}{\pi}\int_{-\pi}^{\pi}h(x)\cos \nu x dx=\frac{1}{\pi}\int_{-\pi}^{\pi}h(x)\sin \nu x dx$$
$$=a_\nu-a_\nu=b_\nu-b_\nu=0. \quad (2.32)$$

† Meschkowski (3), p. 85 or Hyslop, *Infinite Series*, p. 70.
‡ Meschkowski (3), p. 86 or Hyslop, *Infinite Series*, p. 74.

We shall now show that such a function vanishes identically. For if it did not, the continuous function $h(x)$ would have to be non-zero, say *positive*, in a certain sub-interval $[a, b]$ $(-\pi<a<b<\pi)$. $h(x)$ would then have a positive minimum in a sub-interval $[\alpha, \beta]$ $(a<\alpha<\beta<b)$:

$$h(x)>0 \text{ for } x\in[a, b], \qquad h(x)>m \text{ for } x\in[\alpha,\beta]. \tag{2.33}$$

We now define a sequence of functions $p_n(x)$ by making

$$p_n(x) = \{1-2 \sin \tfrac{1}{2}(x-a) \sin \tfrac{1}{2}(x-b)\}^n.$$

Then $p_1(x)>\xi>1$ in the interval $[\alpha, \beta]$, $p_1(a) = p_1(b) = 1$, and $|\, p_1(x)\,| <1$ outside $[a, b]$.

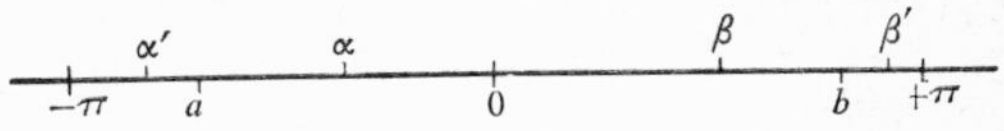

Fig. 6.

If α' and β' satisfy the inequalities (cf. Fig. 6)

$$-\pi<\alpha'<a<\alpha<\beta<b<\beta'<\pi$$

then, for a certain $\eta<1$ we have

$$|p_1(x)|<\eta<1 \tag{2.34}$$

for all $x\in[-\pi, \pi]$ lying outside $[\alpha', \beta']$. The differences $a-\alpha'$ and $b-\beta'$ may be chosen less than a given fixed $\varepsilon>0$:

$$a-\alpha'< \varepsilon, \qquad \beta'-b < \varepsilon. \tag{2.35}$$

If now N is an arbitrary integer,

$$p_n(x)>\xi^n>N \tag{2.36}$$

for $x\in[\alpha, \beta]$ and sufficiently large n, say $n>N_1$. By (2.34) we also have

$$|p_n(x)|<\eta^n<N^{-1}, \tag{2.36$'$}$$

for $n>N_2$, say, and $x\in[-\pi,\alpha')$ or $x\in(\beta', \pi]$. For $n>N_3 = \max(N_1,N_2)$ both inequalities (2.36) and (2.36′) hold, each in its specified interval.

Consider now the integral

$$J(n)=\int_{-\pi}^{\pi} p_n(x)h(x)dx.$$

We break it up into

$$J(n)=J_1(n)+J_2(n)+J_3(n),$$

where

$$J_1(n)=\int_{-\pi}^{\alpha'}+\int_{\beta'}^{\pi}; \quad J_2(n)=\int_{\alpha'}^{a}+\int_{b}^{\beta'}; \quad J_3(n)=\int_{a}^{b}.$$

Let us now estimate the absolute values of these integrals separately. If M is the maximum of the continuous function $|h(x)|$, we have, by (2.35) and (2.36′),

$$|J_1(n)|<\frac{2\pi M}{N}, \qquad |J_2(n)|<2\varepsilon M.$$

Both bounds can be made arbitrarily small by suitable choice of ε and n. On the other hand, by (2.36) J_3 can be made arbitrarily large by choosing n suitably:

$$J_3(n)>Nm(\beta-\alpha).$$

It therefore follows that $J(n)$ is certainly positive provided n is taken sufficiently large.

We now note that the function $p_1(x)$ has the character of a Fourier sum. To see this, let us write it in the form

$$\begin{aligned} p_1(x) &= 1+\cos\{x-\tfrac{1}{2}(a+b)\}-\cos\tfrac{1}{2}(a-b)\\ &= 1-\cos\tfrac{1}{2}(a-b)+\cos\tfrac{1}{2}(a+b)\cos x+\sin\tfrac{1}{2}(a+b)\sin x\\ &= \tfrac{1}{2}a_0+a_1\cos x+b_1\sin x. \end{aligned}$$

Using induction and the addition theorem we can easily prove that $p_n(x)=\{p_1(x)\}^n$ is also a Fourier sum. But we have just shown that

$$J(n)=\int_{-\pi}^{\pi} p_n(x)h(x)dx>0. \tag{2.37}$$

Moreover, by (2.32) we have, for each separate term in this integral,

$$\int_{-\pi}^{\pi} h(x) \cos \nu x dx = \int_{-\pi}^{\pi} h(x) \sin \nu x dx = 0.$$

This contradicts the inequality (2.37). If $h(x) < 0$ we arrive at a corresponding result. Hence the assumption (2.33) is false, and we have in fact

$$g(x) = s(x) = \tfrac{1}{2}a_0 + \sum_{\nu=1}^{\infty} (a_\nu \cos \nu x + b_\nu \sin \nu x).$$

This completes the proof of the representability of continuous functions when the Fourier series converges uniformly. We note that in the course of the proof we have assumed only the continuity, but not the differentiability, of the function.

Let us now return to sectionally smooth functions $f(x)$. If such a function is continuous everywhere, the foregoing results ensure that it can be represented in the form

$$f(x) = \tfrac{1}{2}a_0 + \sum_{\nu=1}^{\infty} (a_\nu \cos \nu x + b_\nu \sin \nu x),$$

where

$$a_\nu = \frac{1}{\pi}\int_{-\pi}^{\pi} f(x) \cos \nu x dx, \qquad b_\nu = \frac{1}{\pi}\int_{-\pi}^{\pi} f(x) \sin \nu x dx.$$

Let us now suppose that the function $f(x)$ has in the interval $[-\pi, \pi]$ a finite number of points of discontinuity x_ρ $(\rho = 1,2,3, \ldots r)$ with saltus $\sigma(x_\rho)$ given by

$$f(x_\rho^+) - f(x_\rho^-) = \sigma_\rho = \sigma(x_\rho).$$

In this case the function

$$F(x) = \sum_{\rho=1}^{r} \frac{\sigma_\rho}{\pi} D(x - x_\rho),$$

where

$$D(x-x_\rho) = \sin(x-x_\rho)+\tfrac{1}{2}\sin 2(x-x_\rho)+\tfrac{1}{3}\sin 3(x-x_\rho)+\dots$$

is the Dirichlet series investigated in § 2.3, has step discontinuities of the same amount and at the same points as the given function $f(x)$.

The function

$$\phi(x) = f(x)-F(x) \tag{2.38}$$

is then continuous and sectionally smooth throughout the interval $[-\pi, \pi]$, although there may be points at which the derivative has a saltus. In accordance with § 2.4, this function possesses a convergent Fourier series, which at the same time represents the function.

Now let a_ν and b_ν be the Fourier coefficients of $f(x)$, A_ν and B_ν those of $F(x)$, and α_ν and β_ν those of $\phi(x)$. Then, by (2.38) we have

$$a_\nu = A_\nu+\alpha_\nu, \qquad b_\nu = B_\nu+\beta_\nu, \qquad \nu = 0,1,2,\dots \tag{2.39}$$

We also have, for all x,

$$F(x) = \tfrac{1}{2}\{F(x^+)+F(x^-)\}, \qquad \phi(x) = \tfrac{1}{2}\{\phi(x^+)+\phi(x^-)\}. \tag{2.40}$$

In the case of $F(x)$ this follows from (2.26), $F(x)$ being a sum of Dirichlet series. For $\phi(x)$ (2.40) is trivial, since the function is continuous. For the Fourier series corresponding to the function $f(x)$ it now follows from (2.39) and (2.40) that

$$\tfrac{1}{2}a_0+\sum_{\nu=1}^{\infty}(a_\nu\cos\nu x+b_\nu\sin\nu x) = \tfrac{1}{2}\{f(x^+)+f(x^-)\}. \tag{2.41}$$

Thus we have shown that *a sectionally smooth function $f(x)$ of period 2π possesses a Fourier series which converges uniformly in every interval in which it is continuous. This series represents the function at all points at which it is* *continuous. At points of discontinuity the series represents the value*

$$\tfrac{1}{2}\{f(x_\rho^+)+f(x_\rho^-)\}.$$

It is immaterial how the function $f(x)$ is defined at the point x_ρ. If $f(x_\rho) = f(x_\rho^+)$, the series still represents the arithmetic mean of $f(x_\rho^-)$ and $f(x_\rho^+)$.

§ 2.6. Example of a divergent Fourier series. So far we have been concerned exclusively with the representation of sectionally smooth functions. The question arises whether it is possible to represent *all* continuous functions by Fourier series.

The investigation of the sufficient conditions for such a representation to be possible turns out to be a matter of some difficulty. Later on we shall deal in greater detail with the question of the conditions under which a function can be approximated in mean by trigonometric polynomials. At present it will suffice to give an example, due to Fejér, of a continuous function for which the corresponding Fourier series does not converge at all points,† thus showing that the continuity of a periodic function is not sufficient to ensure that it can be represented by a Fourier series which converges at all points.‡ We start with the trigonometric sum:

$$f_n(x) = \frac{1}{n}+\frac{\cos x}{n-1}+\frac{\cos 2x}{n-2}+\dots+\frac{\cos (n-1)x}{1}-\left\{\frac{\cos (n+1)x}{1}+\dots+\frac{\cos 2nx}{n}\right\}$$

$$= \sum_{k=1}^{n}\frac{1}{k}\{\cos (n-k)x-\cos (n+k)x\}. \qquad (2.42)$$

† For further discussion of the convergence of Fourier series see e.g. Carslaw, *Introduction to the Theory of Fourier's Series and Integrals*, or Hardy and Rogosinski, *Fourier Series*.

‡ We distinguish point convergence from mean convergence, cf. p. 16.

This can be transformed by the addition theorem to give

$$f_n(x) = 2 \sin nx \sum_{k=1}^{n} \frac{\sin kx}{k}.$$

From the fact that the Dirichlet series (2.19) converges we at once see that the sums $f_n(x)$ are *uniformly* bounded, so that

$$|f_n(x)| < M. \qquad (2.43)$$

We now define a new function $F(x)$ by

$$F(x) = \sum_{n=1}^{\infty} \frac{g_n(x)}{n^2}, \qquad g_n(x) = f_N(x), \qquad (2.44)$$

where the suffix N is 2^{n^3}.

By (2.43) the terms of the series (2.44) are each less than those of a convergent series; hence the series (2.44) converges uniformly in any closed interval of the x-axis. Thus $F(x)$ is a continuous function.† It is even, and has period 2π. By (2.15) and (2.15′) the Fourier coefficients of this function $F(x)$ are

$$b_\nu = 0, \qquad a_\nu = \frac{2}{\pi}\int_0^\pi F(x) \cos \nu x dx$$

$$= \sum_{n=1}^{\infty} \frac{1}{n^2} \frac{2}{\pi} \int_0^\pi g_n(x) \cos \nu x dx = \sum_{n=1}^{\infty} \frac{a_\nu^{(n)}}{n^2},$$

where $a_\nu^{(n)}$ is the corresponding Fourier coefficient of $g_n(x)$.

Thus the partial sums of the Fourier series of $F(x)$ are obtained by combining the corresponding partial sums of the series of $g_n(x)$:

$$S_m(x) = \tfrac{1}{2}a_0 + \sum_{\nu=1}^{m} a_\nu \cos \nu x = \sum_{n=1}^{\infty} \frac{1}{2} \frac{a_0^{(n)}}{n^2} + \sum_{n=1}^{\infty} \sum_{\nu=1}^{m} \frac{a_\nu^{(n)}}{n^2} \cos \nu x$$

$$= \sum_{n=1}^{\infty} \frac{s_m^{(n)}(x)}{n^2}.$$

† See, e.g. Meschkowski (3), p. 86 or Hyslop, *Infinite Series*, p. 74.

Now suppose $s_m^{(n)} = s_m^{(n)}(0)$. Then we have, in particular, by (2.42)

$$s_n^{(n)} = 1+\tfrac{1}{2}+\tfrac{1}{3}+\ \dots\ +\frac{1}{2^{n^3}}.$$

We can readily find a lower bound for this sequence: †

$$s_n^{(n)} > \int_1^{2^{n^3}} \frac{dx}{x} = n^3 \ln 2. \tag{2.46}$$

Now let S_n be the corresponding sums of the Fourier series of $F(x)$, again evaluated at the point $x = 0$. Since the terms $s_m^{(n)}$ are non-negative throughout, we see, by (2.46), and taking account only of the term $n = m$ in the sum

$$\sum_{n=1}^{\infty} \frac{s_m^{(n)}}{n^2},$$

that

$$S_n \geqslant \frac{s_n^{(n)}}{n^2} > n \ln 2.$$

That is to say, the Fourier series of the continuous function $F(x)$ diverges at the point $x = 0$.

§ 2.7. Exercises

1. Find the Fourier series of the periodic functions of period 2π defined in the interval $[-\pi, \pi]$ by

(i) $f(x) = x.$

(ii) $f(x) = \begin{cases} 0 & \text{for } -\pi \leqslant x < 0, \\ \sin x & \text{for } \quad 0 \leqslant x < \pi. \end{cases}$

(iii) $f(x) = x^2.$

(iv) $f(x) = x^3.$

(v) $f(x) = x \cos x.$

† Cf. Meschkowski (3) p. 27 or Hyslop, *Infinite Series*, p. 39.

2. Find the Fourier series of the periodic functions of period 2π defined in the interval $[0, 2\pi]$ by

(i) $f(x) = \dfrac{\pi^2}{6} - \dfrac{\pi x}{2} + \dfrac{x^2}{4}$.

(ii) $f(x) = \ln \{2(1-\cos x)\}^{\frac{1}{2}}$.

(iii) $f(x) = x^2$.

CHAPTER III

EXAMPLES AND APPLICATIONS

§ 3.1. Transformation of the interval of periodicity. The periodic function of period 2π defined in the interval $[-\pi, \pi]$ by

$$f_3(x) = \begin{cases} +1 \text{ for } -\pi < x < -\tfrac{1}{2}\pi, & 0 < x < \tfrac{1}{2}\pi, \\ -1 \text{ for } -\tfrac{1}{2}\pi < x < 0, & \tfrac{1}{2}\pi < x < \pi, \\ \;\;0 \text{ for } x = \tfrac{1}{2}n\pi, & n = 0, \pm 1, \pm 2, \ldots \end{cases}$$

is an odd function, so that $f_3(-x) = -f_3(x)$ (Fig. 7).

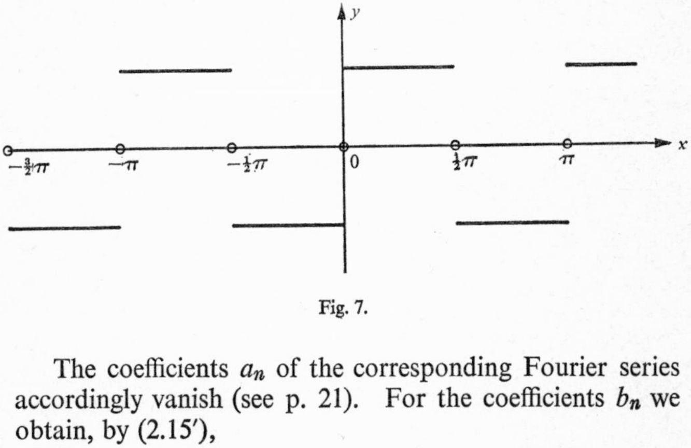

Fig. 7.

The coefficients a_n of the corresponding Fourier series accordingly vanish (see p. 21). For the coefficients b_n we obtain, by (2.15′),

$$b_n = \frac{2}{\pi}\int_0^{\frac{1}{2}\pi} \sin nx dx - \frac{2}{\pi}\int_{\frac{1}{2}\pi}^{\pi} \sin nx dx,$$

from which the series expansion of $f_3(x)$ follows, in the form

$$f_3(x) = \frac{4}{\pi}(\sin 2x + \tfrac{1}{3}\sin 6x + \tfrac{1}{5}\sin 10x + \ldots).$$

The function defined for all real values of x by $f_4(x) = |\sin x|$ is an even function. In this case we have

$$a_n = \frac{2}{\pi}\int_0^{\pi} \sin x \cos nx dx,$$

from which it follows that

$$f_4(x) = \frac{2}{\pi} - \frac{4}{\pi}\sum_{n=1}^{\infty} \frac{\cos 2nx}{4n^2-1}.$$

We have already pointed out that the integrals for calculating the coefficients a_n and b_n of a Fourier series can be taken over an arbitrary interval of length 2π (cf. 2.27)). If the function to be expanded is given for the interval $[0, 2\pi]$, it is natural to integrate over that interval in calculating the coefficients.

Again, suppose that $f_5(x) = e^x$ for $0 \leqslant x < 2\pi$, and $f_5(x+2\pi) = f_5(x)$. In this case we have

$$a_n = \frac{1}{\pi}\int_0^{2\pi} e^x \cos nx dx, \qquad b_n = \frac{1}{\pi}\int_0^{2\pi} e^x \sin nx dx,$$

and evaluation of these integrals leads to the series †

$$f_5(x) \sim \frac{e^{2\pi}-1}{\pi}\left\{\frac{1}{2} + \sum_{n=1}^{\infty} \frac{1}{1+n^2}(\cos nx - n \sin nx)\right\}.$$

By a slight modification of this procedure a trigonometric series can also be obtained for sectionally smooth functions of period $p \neq 2\pi$. For the interval $0 \leqslant x \leqslant 2\pi$ is transformed by the substitution $x = 2\pi y/p$ into the interval $0 \leqslant y \leqslant p$, and the coefficients a_n and b_n become

$$a_n = \frac{1}{\pi}\int_0^{2\pi} f(x) \cos nx dx = \frac{2}{p}\int_0^{p} f\left(\frac{2\pi y}{p}\right) \cos \frac{2\pi n y}{p} dy,$$

$$b_n = \frac{1}{\pi}\int_0^{2\pi} f(x) \sin nx dx = \frac{2}{p}\int_0^{p} f\left(\frac{2\pi y}{p}\right) \sin \frac{2\pi n y}{p} dy.$$

† For $x \neq 2\pi n$, the sign $\sim$ can be replaced by $=$.

If we put $f(2\pi y/p) = g(y)$, we have for the function $g(y)$, of period p, a series representation of the form

$$g(y) \sim \tfrac{1}{2}a_0 + \sum_{n=1}^{\infty}\left(a_n \cos\frac{2\pi ny}{p} + b_n \sin\frac{2\pi ny}{p}\right), \qquad (3.1)$$

with coefficients

$$a_n = \frac{2}{p}\int_0^p g(y)\cos\frac{2\pi ny}{p}\,dy, \quad b_n = \frac{2}{p}\int_0^p g(y)\sin\frac{2\pi ny}{p}\,dy. \quad (3.2)$$

Since, conversely, any sectionally smooth function $g(y)$ of period p can be transformed by the substitution $y = px/2\pi$ into a corresponding function $g(px/2\pi) = f(x)$ of period 2π, we have, for all sectionally smooth functions of period p, the representation (3.1) with coefficients (3.2). At all points of continuity the series (3.1) represents the function.

Let us take as an example the function

$$f_6(x) = x - [x],$$

where $[x]$ is the greatest integer not exceeding x. This function has period 1, and by (3.1) and (3.2) we obtain the representation

$$f_6(x) \sim \tfrac{1}{2} - \frac{1}{\pi}\sum_{n=1}^{\infty}\frac{\sin 2\pi nx}{n}, \qquad x \neq n.$$

Our function $f_6(x)$ vanishes for all integral $x = n$; the corresponding series does not represent the value 0 of the function for $x = 0, \pm 1, \pm 2, \dots$, but by the theorem of § 2.5 the value $\tfrac{1}{2}\{f(n^+)+f(n^-)\} = \tfrac{1}{2}$.

Let $\{x\}$ be the absolute value of the difference between x and the nearest integer. The Fourier series of this even function $f_7(x) = \{x\}$ of 'saw-tooth' form is readily shown to be

$$f_7(x) = \tfrac{1}{4} - \frac{2}{\pi^2}\sum_{n=0}^{\infty}\frac{\cos(2n+1)2\pi x}{(2n+1)^2}.$$

Putting $x = \frac{1}{2}$ we obtain from this the remarkable series for π:

$$\frac{\pi^2}{8} = 1 + \frac{1}{3^2} + \frac{1}{5^2} + \frac{1}{7^2} + \ldots.$$

Fig. 8 shows the graph of the function $f_7(x)$.

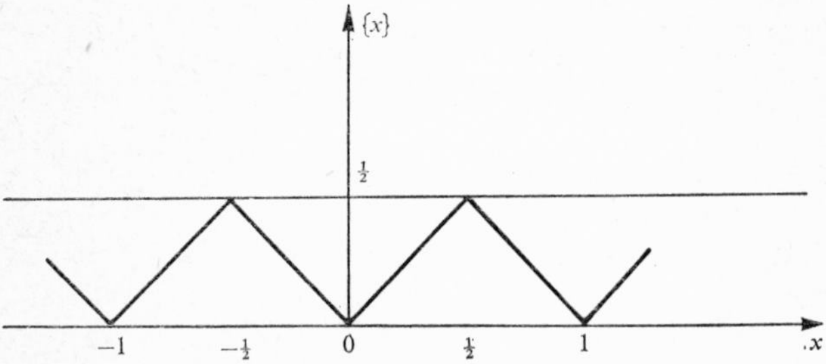

Fig. 8.

§ 3.2. Complex form of Fourier series. For some applications it is convenient to introduce a complex notation for Fourier series. We first define Fourier coefficients a_n and b_n (in the interval $[-\pi, \pi]$) for negative indices.

$$\begin{aligned} a_{-\nu} &= \frac{1}{\pi}\int_{-\pi}^{\pi} f(x)\cos(-\nu x)dx = a_\nu, \\ b_{-\nu} &= \frac{1}{\pi}\int_{-\pi}^{\pi} f(x)\sin(-\nu x)dx = -b_\nu. \end{aligned} \tag{3.3}$$

We then put

$$\alpha_\nu = \tfrac{1}{2}(a_\nu - ib_\nu) \tag{3.4}$$

for all integral ν. In particular, we have

$$\alpha_0 = \tfrac{1}{2}a_0. \tag{3.4'}$$

Then †

$$\alpha_\nu e^{i\nu x} = \tfrac{1}{2}(a_\nu - ib_\nu)(\cos \nu x + i \sin \nu x),$$
$$\alpha_{-\nu} e^{-i\nu x} = \tfrac{1}{2}(a_\nu + ib_\nu)(\cos \nu x - i \sin \nu x),$$

and therefore

$$\alpha_\nu e^{i\nu x} + \alpha_{-\nu} e^{-i\nu x} = a_\nu \cos \nu x + b_\nu \sin \nu x.$$

Hence the series

$$\tfrac{1}{2}a_0 + \sum_{\nu=1}^{\infty} (a_\nu \cos \nu x + b_\nu \sin \nu x)$$

becomes

$$\sum_{\nu=-\infty}^{\infty} \alpha_\nu e^{i\nu x} \tag{4.5}$$

with

$$\alpha_\nu = \frac{1}{2\pi}\int_{-\pi}^{\pi} f(x) e^{-i\nu x} dx, \qquad \nu = 0, \pm 1, \pm 2, \ldots \tag{4.6}$$

This form is particularly useful when the function to be represented can be simply expressed by means of the exponential function.

Consider, as an example, the function of period 2π given in the interval $[-\pi, \pi]$ by

$$f_8(x) = \cos \lambda x,$$

where λ is real and *non-integral.*

In this case

$$\alpha_\nu = \frac{1}{4\pi}\int_{-\pi}^{\pi} \{e^{i(\lambda-\nu)x} + e^{-i(\lambda+\nu)x}\} dx$$

$$= \frac{1}{4\pi i(\lambda-\nu)}\Big[e^{i(\lambda-\nu)x}\Big]_{-\pi}^{\pi} - \frac{1}{4\pi i(\lambda+\nu)}\Big[e^{-i(\lambda+\nu)x}\Big]_{-\pi}^{\pi},$$

† Here we are using the formulae $\cos x = \frac{1}{2}(e^{ix} + e^{-ix})$, $\sin x = \frac{1}{2}(e^{ix} - e^{-ix})/i$, which are readily derivable from the power series for e^x, $\sin x$ and $\cos x$.

or

$$\alpha_\nu = \frac{1}{2\pi}\left\{\frac{1}{\lambda-\nu}\sin(\lambda-\nu)\pi + \frac{1}{\lambda+\nu}\sin(\lambda+\nu)\pi\right\}. \quad (3.6')$$

This is a real quantity. We therefore have by (3.4) and (3.6′),

$$b_\nu = 0, \qquad \nu = 1,2,3,\ldots,$$

$$a_\nu = \frac{2(-1)^\nu \lambda \sin \lambda\pi}{\pi(\lambda^2-\nu^2)}, \qquad \nu = 0,1,2,\ldots \quad (3.7)$$

Thus we obtain for the given function the Fourier series

$$\cos \lambda x = \frac{2\lambda \sin \lambda\pi}{\pi}\left\{\frac{1}{2\lambda^2} - \frac{\cos x}{\lambda^2-1^2} + \frac{\cos 2x}{\lambda^2-2^2} - \ldots\right\}. \quad (3.8)$$

Since $\cos \lambda x$ is an even function, the series is continuous, even at $x = \pm n\pi$.

§ 3.3. The representation of sin πx as a product. A number of remarkable deductions can be made from the result (3.8). If in (3.8) we put π for x, and then regard λ as variable, we obtain, on writing x for this variable,

$$\cot \pi x = \frac{2x}{\pi}\left(\frac{1}{2x^2} + \frac{1}{x^2-1^2} + \frac{1}{x^2-2^2} + \ldots\right)$$

or

$$\cot \pi x - \frac{1}{\pi x} = -\frac{2x}{\pi}\left(\frac{1}{1^2-x^2} + \frac{1}{2^2-x^2} + \ldots\right). \quad (3.9)$$

We can find an upper bound for the general term of this series as follows. We have, for $n > x\sqrt{2}$,

$$\frac{1}{n^2-x^2} < \frac{2}{n^2}.$$

Hence the series (3.9) converges for all $x \neq 0, \pm 1, \pm 2, \pm 3, \ldots$. The convergence is clearly uniform in any interval of the x-axis which does not contain any integers. Term-by-term integration leads, for $0<a<x<1$, to

$$\pi\int_a^x\left(\cot \pi t-\frac{1}{\pi t}\right)dt = \ln\frac{\sin \pi x}{\pi x}-\ln\frac{\sin \pi a}{\pi a}$$

$$=\sum_{\nu=1}^{\infty}\ln\frac{\nu^2-x^2}{\nu^2-a^2}.$$

Proceeding to the limit $a\to 0$, we obtain

$$\ln\frac{\sin \pi x}{\pi x}=\sum_{\nu=1}^{\infty}\ln\left(1-\frac{x^2}{\nu^2}\right),$$

that is,

$$\sin \pi x = \pi x\prod_{\nu=1}^{\infty}\left(1-\frac{x^2}{\nu^2}\right). \tag{3.10}$$

This representation of the function $\sin \pi x$ as a product has thus been derived in the first place for values of x in an interval of the real axis. But since the infinite product

$$\prod_{\nu=1}^{\infty}\left(1-\frac{z^2}{\nu^2}\right)$$

converges † for all complex values of z, equation (3.10) holds, by the principle of permanence of form in the theory of functions, for arbitrary regions of the complex plane containing the interval $0<x<1$, in which the function $\sin \pi z$ and the product are regular.

The equation (3.10) accordingly holds for arbitrary complex numbers $z = x+iy$, so that

$$\sin \pi z = \pi z\prod_{\nu=1}^{\infty}\left(1-\frac{z^2}{\nu^2}\right). \tag{3.10'}$$

† Meschkowski (3), IX or Hyslop, *Infinite Series*, p. 98.

If in (3.10) we substitute $\frac{1}{2}$ for x, we obtain Wallis's formula for π as an infinite product:

$$\frac{\pi}{2} = \prod_{\nu=1}^{\infty} \frac{2\nu}{2\nu-1} \cdot \frac{2\nu}{2\nu+1} = \frac{2}{1} \cdot \frac{2}{3} \cdot \frac{4}{3} \cdot \frac{4}{5} \cdot \frac{6}{5} \cdot \frac{6}{7} \cdot \frac{8}{7} \cdots$$

§ 3.4. Parseval's equation. Let $f(x)$ and $g(x)$ be two sectionally smooth functions of period 2π, and let a_ν, b_ν and α_ν, β_ν be their respective Fourier coefficients. Then Parseval's formula holds:

$$\tfrac{1}{2}a_0\alpha_0 + \sum_{\nu=1}^{\infty} (a_\nu\alpha_\nu + b_\nu\beta_\nu) = \frac{1}{\pi}\int_{-\pi}^{\pi} fg\,dx. \qquad (3.11)$$

To prove (3.11) we go back to Bessel's inequality (2.12). Since the function $f(x)$ is sectionally smooth, it can be represented at all points of continuity by the corresponding Fourier series:

$$f(x) = \tfrac{1}{2}a_0 + \sum_{\nu=1}^{\infty} (a_\nu \cos \nu x + b_\nu \sin \nu x).$$

Calculation of the integrand in

$$\int_{-\pi}^{\pi} \left\{ f(x) - \tfrac{1}{2}a_0 - \sum_{\nu=1}^{\infty} (a_\nu \cos \nu x + b_\nu \sin \nu x) \right\}^2 dx = 0$$

by the method of § 2.1 then leads to Bessel's equation

$$\frac{1}{\pi}\int_{-\pi}^{\pi} f^2 dx = \tfrac{1}{2}a_0^2 + \sum_{\nu=1}^{\infty} (a_\nu^2 + b_\nu^2). \qquad (3.12)$$

Thus for sectionally smooth functions the sign of equality is to be taken in (2.12). To complete the proof of (3.11) we now evaluate the integral

$$\frac{1}{\pi}\int_{-\pi}^{\pi} (f+g)^2 dx = \frac{1}{\pi}\int_{-\pi}^{\pi} f^2 dx + \frac{2}{\pi}\int_{-\pi}^{\pi} fg\,dx + \frac{1}{\pi}\int_{-\pi}^{\pi} g^2 dx.$$

Taking account of (3.12), we then obtain

$$\frac{1}{\pi}\int_{-\pi}^{\pi} g^2 dx = \tfrac{1}{2}\alpha_0^2 + \sum_{\nu=1}^{\infty} (\alpha_\nu^2 + \beta_\nu^2),$$

$$\frac{2}{\pi}\int_{-\pi}^{\pi} fg dx = \tfrac{1}{2}(a_0+\alpha_0)^2 + \sum_{\nu=1}^{\infty} \{(a_\nu+\alpha_\nu)^2 + (b_\nu+\beta_\nu)^2\}$$

$$-\tfrac{1}{2}a_0^2 - \tfrac{1}{2}\alpha_0^2 - \sum_{\nu=1}^{\infty} (\alpha_\nu^2+\beta_\nu^2) - \sum_{\nu=1}^{\infty} (a_\nu^2+b_\nu^2),$$

from which (3.11) follows.

§ **3.5. The isoperimetric problem.** We shall apply the formula (3.11) to solve the isoperimetric problem in the plane. This problem can be formulated as follows.

Consider the set **S** *of simple closed rectifiable plane curves* **C** *of length L. It is required to find the curve of the set* **S** *for which the area A(***C***) of the region enclosed is a maximum.*

J. Steiner (1796-1863) showed by elementary methods that, corresponding to any curve $\mathbf{C}\in\mathbf{S}$ which is *not* a circle, it is possible to find a " better " curve $\mathbf{C}_1\in\mathbf{S}$, that is, a curve of length L for which the enclosed area $A(\mathbf{C}_1)<A(\mathbf{C})$. He believed that by establishing this he had proved that the circle was the solution of the isoperimetric problem; there was no question of any other curve being the solution.

K. Weierstrass pointed out that Steiner's argument was not conclusive; we have to reckon with the possibility that no curve exists with the required extremal property.†

† The following argument, due to Perron, illustrates this. Using Steiner's method we could show that 1 is the greatest of the integers. For any integer not equal to 1 is increased by squaring it: $n^2>n$ for $n>1$. Every integer not equal to 1 can therefore (by taking n^2) be ' improved ' (here meaning ' increased '). Hence, etc. In this case the error is obvious; the assumption that a greatest integer exists is fallacious.

It is indeed possible to pass from Steiner's result, by rather complicated considerations involving limits, to a rigorous proof that the circle represents the solution of the isoperimetric problem. Much simpler, however, is the elegant solution due to Hurwitz, who makes use of the theory of Fourier series. Let us assume that a curve **C**∈**S** is given in parametric form by

$$x = x(t), \quad y = y(t),$$

where the functions $x(t)$, $y(t)$ and their first derivatives are sectionally smooth. For the parameter t we choose

$$t = \frac{2\pi s}{L}, \tag{3.13}$$

where L is the length of the whole curve **C**, s the arc-length measured from any point P∈**C** up to the point of parameter t. The functions $x(t)$ and $y(t)$ then have period 2π and can therefore be expressed as Fourier series, in the form

$$\begin{aligned} x(t) &= \sum_{\nu=1}^{\infty} (a_\nu \cos \nu t + b_\nu \sin \nu t), \\ y(t) &= \sum_{\nu=1}^{\infty} (\alpha_\nu \cos \nu t + \beta_\nu \sin \nu t). \end{aligned} \tag{3.14}$$

Since a translation is irrelevant in the isoperimetric problem, we can take $a_0 = \alpha_0 = 0$ in (3.14).

By differentiation it follows that

$$\begin{aligned} x'(t) &= \sum_{\nu=1}^{\infty} \nu(b_\nu \cos \nu t - a_\nu \sin \nu t), \\ y'(t) &= \sum_{\nu=1}^{\infty} \nu(\beta_\nu \cos \nu t - \alpha_\nu \sin \nu t). \end{aligned} \tag{3.15}$$

Furthermore, by (3.13),

$$\{x'(t)\}^2 + \{y'(t)\}^2 = \left(\frac{ds}{dt}\right)^2 = \frac{L^2}{4\pi^2}. \tag{3.16}$$

We now apply Bessel's equation (3.12) to the Fourier series (3.15) and obtain, having regard to (3.16),

$$\frac{L^2}{2\pi^2} = \frac{1}{\pi}\int_0^{2\pi} [\{x'(t)\}^2 + \{y'(t)\}^2]dt$$
$$= \sum_{\nu=1}^{\infty} \nu^2(a_\nu^2 + b_\nu^2 + \alpha_\nu^2 + \beta_\nu^2). \tag{3.17}$$

For the area A enclosed by the curve **C**, namely

$$A = \int_0^{2\pi} x(t)y'(t)dt,$$

we have, by Parseval's equation (3.11) applied to the functions $x(t)$ and $y'(t)$ and by (3.14) and (3.15),

$$A = \pi \sum_{\nu=1}^{\infty} \nu(a_\nu\beta_\nu - b_\nu\alpha_\nu). \tag{3.18}$$

It then follows from (3.17) and (3.18) that

$$L^2 - 4\pi A = 2\pi^2 \sum_{\nu=1}^{\infty} \{(\nu a_\nu - \beta_\nu)^2 + (\nu\alpha_\nu + b_\nu)^2 + (\nu^2 - 1)(b_\nu^2 + \beta_\nu^2)\}. \tag{3.19}$$

Clearly the right-hand side of (3.19) can never become negative, so that we obtain from (3.19) the isoperimetric inequality

$$L^2 - 4\pi A \geqslant 0. \tag{3.20}$$

We now inquire when the sign of equality holds in this relation. The necessary and sufficient condition for this is obviously that for all $\nu > 1$,

$$\beta_\nu = b_\nu = \alpha_\nu = a_\nu = 0, \tag{3.21}$$

while for $\nu = 1$,

$$a_1 = \beta_1, \qquad \alpha_1 = -b_1. \tag{3.21'}$$

In this case we have

$$x(t) = a_1 \cos t + b_1 \sin t,$$
$$y(t) = -b_1 \cos t + a_1 \sin t,$$

that is,

$$\{x(t)\}^2+\{y(t)\}^2 = a_1^2+b_1^2.$$

The curve **C** is thus a circle In this case (3.20) does in fact hold with the sign of equality.

Hence by (3.20) we have, for every curve **C** that is not a circle,

$$A(\mathbf{C})<\frac{L^2}{4\pi} = A(\mathbf{C}_0),$$

where $\mathbf{C}_0$ is the circle of circumference L.

It can now be shown that all rectifiable curves of length L can be approximated to any degree of accuracy by curves of the type considered here. It then follows that the inequality (3.20) holds for all curves of the class of rectifiable curves. Thus the solution of the problem is complete.

§ 3.6. Calculation of given sums. So far we have determined the Fourier series corresponding to given periodic functions. But it is sometimes necessary to solve the converse problem, in which a Fourier series, for instance

$$u(x) = \frac{\cos 2x}{3}-\frac{\cos 3x}{8}+\ldots+(-1)^n\frac{\cos nx}{n^2-1}+\ldots, \quad (3.22)$$

is given and an explicit expression for the sum $u(x)$ is required. A possible method of solving such problems in certain cases is by way of the theory of analytic functions in the complex plane.

It is well-known that a function regular inside and on the unit circle, $|z|\leqslant 1$, can be expressed as a power series whose radius of convergence is greater than 1. Let

$$f(z) = A_0+A_1z+A_2z^2+\ldots \quad (3.23)$$

be such a series, having all its coefficients real. If we put

$$z = e^{i\phi} = \cos\phi+i\sin\phi,$$

(3.23) becomes, since $(\cos\phi+i\sin\phi)^n = \cos n\phi+i\sin n\phi$,

$$f(z) = \sum_{\nu=0}^{\infty} A_\nu(\cos\nu\phi+i\sin\nu\phi).$$

Separating real and imaginary parts, we obtain from this two Fourier series

$$u(\phi) = \mathrm{Re}\, f(z) = A_0+A_1\cos\phi+A_2\cos 2\phi+\ldots \qquad (3.24)$$

$$v(\phi) = \mathrm{Im}\, f(z) = \qquad A_1\sin\phi+A_2\sin 2\phi+\ldots \qquad (3.24')$$

Let us consider an example. The series

$$\ln(1+z) = z-\frac{z^2}{2}+\frac{z^3}{3}-\frac{z^4}{4}+\ldots$$

converges for $|z|<1$, but also for $|z| = 1$, except when $z = -1$. If we write x for ϕ, the series (3.24) and (3.24′) become

$$\mathrm{Re}\ln(1+e^{ix}) = \cos x-\frac{\cos 2x}{2}+\frac{\cos 3x}{3}-\ldots \qquad (3.25)$$

$$\mathrm{Im}\ln(1+e^{ix}) = \sin x-\frac{\sin 2x}{2}+\frac{\sin 3x}{3}-\ldots \qquad (3.25')$$

for all $x \neq (2k+1)\pi$.

Now

$$1+e^{ix} = 1+\cos x+i\sin x = 2\cos^2\tfrac{1}{2}x+2i\sin\tfrac{1}{2}x\cos\tfrac{1}{2}x$$
$$= 2\cos\tfrac{1}{2}x(\cos\tfrac{1}{2}x+i\sin\tfrac{1}{2}x). \qquad (3.26)$$

Since

$$\ln w = \ln|w|+i\arg w,$$

it follows from (3.26) that

$$\ln(1+e^{ix}) = \ln(2\cos\tfrac{1}{2}x)+\tfrac{1}{2}ix, \qquad (3.26')$$

and (3.25) and (3.25′) become

$$\ln(2\cos\tfrac{1}{2}x) = \cos x-\frac{\cos 2x}{2}+\frac{\cos 3x}{3}-\ldots \qquad (3.27)$$

$$\tfrac{1}{2}x = \sin x-\frac{\sin 2x}{2}+\frac{\sin 3x}{3}-\ldots \qquad (3.27')$$

If, conversely, a Fourier series is given, say the series (3.22), we can try to determine the corresponding function $f(z)$ having the power series expansion (3.23). For this purpose we first write down the sine series associated with (3.22):

$$v(x) = \frac{\sin 2x}{3} - \frac{\sin 3x}{8} + \ldots + (-1)^n \frac{\sin nx}{n^2-1} + \ldots \qquad (3.22')$$

and then form the sum

$$f(x) = u(x) + iv(x) = \frac{e^{2ix}}{3} - \frac{e^{3ix}}{8} + \ldots + (-1)^n \frac{e^{inx}}{n^2-1} + \ldots \qquad (3.28)$$

or

$$f(x) = g(w) = \frac{w^2}{3} - \frac{w^3}{8} + \ldots + (-1)^n \frac{w^n}{n^2-1} + \ldots \qquad (3.29)$$

where

$$w = e^{ix} = \cos x + i \sin x, \qquad w^{-1} = \cos x - i \sin x. \quad (3.30)$$

Since

$$\frac{1}{n^2-1} = \frac{1}{2}\left(\frac{1}{n-1} - \frac{1}{n+1}\right),$$

(3.29) becomes

$$2g(w) = \left(\frac{w^2}{1} - \frac{w^3}{2} + \frac{w^4}{3} - \ldots\right) - \left(\frac{w^2}{3} - \frac{w^3}{4} + \ldots\right)$$

$$= \left(w - \frac{1}{w}\right)\left(w - \frac{w^2}{2} + \frac{w^3}{3} - \ldots\right) + \left(1 - \frac{w}{2}\right).$$

By (3.28), (3.30) and (3.26′) we can write this result in the alternative form

$$2\{u(x) + iv(x)\} = 2i \sin x\{ln\,(2 \cos \tfrac{1}{2}x) + \tfrac{1}{2}ix\} + 1 - \\ - \tfrac{1}{2}(\cos x + i \sin x).$$

Taking the real parts of both sides, we finally obtain

$$2u(x) = -x \sin x + 1 - \tfrac{1}{2} \cos x,$$

or, for $0 \leqslant x \leqslant 2\pi$,

$$u(x) = \sum_{n=2}^{\infty} (-1)^n \frac{\cos nx}{n^2-1} = \tfrac{1}{2} - \tfrac{1}{4} \cos x - \tfrac{1}{2} x \sin x. \qquad (3.31)$$

This method can always be applied when the sum of the resulting power series (3.23) is known.

A second example, which is simpler, will now be given. Consider

$$v(x) = \sum_{n=1}^{\infty} a^n \sin nx, \qquad 0 < a < 1. \qquad (3.32)$$

In this case

$$u(x) = \sum_{n=1}^{\infty} a^n \cos nx$$

and

$$g(w) = \sum_{n=1}^{\infty} a^n w^n = \frac{aw}{1-aw}.$$

Hence

$$v(x) = \operatorname{Im} g(w) = \frac{a \sin x}{1 - 2a \cos x + a^2}.$$

§ 3.7. Exercises

1. Find the Fourier series of the periodic functions of period 1, defined in the interval [0, 1] by :

(a) $f(x) = \begin{cases} \sin \tfrac{1}{2} \pi x & \text{for } 0 \leqslant x \leqslant \tfrac{1}{2}, \\ -\sin \tfrac{1}{2} \pi x & \text{for } \tfrac{1}{2} < x \leqslant 1. \end{cases}$

(b) $f(x) = \begin{cases} \sin \tfrac{1}{2} \pi x & \text{for } 0 \leqslant x \leqslant \tfrac{1}{2}, \\ 0 & \text{for } \tfrac{1}{2} < x \leqslant 1. \end{cases}$

(c) $f(x) = \begin{cases} x & \text{for } 0 \leqslant x \leqslant \tfrac{1}{2}, \\ 1-x & \text{for } \tfrac{1}{2} < x \leqslant 1. \end{cases}$

2. Obtain series for $\pi^2/6$ and $\pi^2/12$ from the Fourier series for $f(x) = x^2$ $(-\pi \leqslant x < \pi)$.

3. Establish the partial fraction series

$$\frac{\pi}{\sin \pi z} = \frac{1}{z} + \sum_{n=1}^{\infty} (-1)^n \left\{ \frac{1}{z-n} + \frac{1}{z+n} \right\}$$

for all $z \neq 0, \pm 1, \pm 2, \ldots$.

4. Find the Fourier series expansions of

$$f_9(x) = \cosh x = \tfrac{1}{2}(e^x + e^{-x}), \quad (-\pi \leqslant x \leqslant \pi),$$

$$f_{10}(x) = \sinh x = \tfrac{1}{2}(e^x - e^{-x}), \quad (-\pi \leqslant x < \pi).$$

5. Obtain a series for $\pi^2/32$ from the series for x^3 in the interval $[-\pi, \pi]$ (Exercise 3 of Chapter II).

6. Obtain a series for $\pi^2/6$ from the series for x^2 in the interval $[0, 2\pi]$.

7. Use the method of § 3.6 to determine the sums of the following series:

(a) $$\sum_{n=2}^{\infty} (-1)^n \frac{n \sin nx}{n^2 - 1}, \qquad (-\pi \leqslant x < \pi),$$

(b) $$\sum_{n=0}^{\infty} \frac{1}{2^n} \cos nx, \qquad (-\pi \leqslant x < \pi).$$

CHAPTER IV

ORTHONORMAL SYSTEMS

§ 4.1. Definitions. The relation (2.6),

$$\frac{1}{\pi}\int_{-\pi}^{\pi} \sin \nu x \sin \mu x dx = \frac{1}{\pi}\int_{-\pi}^{\pi} \cos \nu x \cos \mu x dx = \delta_{\nu\mu},$$

which is basic to the theory of Fourier series, recalls a familiar formula of analytical geometry; if $\mathbf{e}_\nu$ ($\nu = 1,2,3, \ldots, n$) is a system of mutually orthogonal unit vectors in n-dimensional space, it is well-known that

$$(\mathbf{e}_\nu,\mathbf{e}_\mu) = \delta_{\nu\mu} = \begin{cases} 1 \text{ for } \nu = \mu \\ 0 \text{ for } \nu \neq \mu \end{cases} \tag{4.1}$$

where **(a,b)** is the scalar product of the two vectors **a** and **b.** If the scalar product of two non-zero vectors vanishes, the vectors are mutually perpendicular. This suggests introducing the same terminology for systems of functions.†

The integral

$$(f,g) = \int_a^b f(x)g(x)dx \tag{4.2}$$

is called the **scalar product** of the functions $f(x)$ and $g(x)$ in the interval $[a, b]$. The functions are said to be **orthogonal** if

$$(f,g) = \int_a^b f(x)g(x)dx = 0.$$

† In what follows we confine ourselves, unless the contrary is stated, to systems of *continuous* functions. The integrals are (in the meantime) always to be understood as Riemann integrals.

The non-negative quantity

$$\| f \| = +\sqrt{(f,f)} = +\sqrt{\left\{\int_a^b f^2 dx\right\}} \qquad (4.2')$$

is called the **norm** of $f(x)$. A function is said to be **normalised** if

$$\| f \|^2 = (f,f) = 1.$$

Any function $f(x)$ for which $\| f \|$ does not vanish can be normalised; that is to say, we can find a function $g(x) = cf(x)$ having unit norm; we merely have to take $c = \| f \|^{-1}$.

Using this terminology we can say that the functions

$$(\pi)^{-\frac{1}{2}} \sin \nu x \qquad (\nu = 1,2,3, \ldots) \qquad (4.3)$$

and

$$(\pi)^{-\frac{1}{2}} \cos \nu x \qquad (\nu = 1,2,3, \ldots) \qquad (4.3')$$

are systems of normalised and mutually orthogonal functions in the interval $[-\pi, +\pi]$. Sets of functions of this kind are referred to briefly as **orthonormal systems.**

Such orthonormal systems possess some remarkable properties, which we already found in Chapter II for the systems (4.3) and (4.3′). We shall now see that these properties are typical of *all* orthonormal systems.

Let $\phi_\nu(x)$ $(\nu = 1,2,3, \ldots)$ be an orthonormal system in the interval $[a, b]$, so that

$$(\phi_\nu, \phi_\mu) = \int_a^b \phi_\nu(x)\phi_\mu(x)dx = \delta_{\nu\mu}. \qquad (4.4)$$

Let us assume that a function $f(x)$ is represented in $[a, b]$ by a uniformly convergent series

$$f(x) = a_1\phi_1(x) + a_2\phi_2(x) + a_3\phi_3(x) + \ldots \qquad (4.5)$$

Then † by (4.4)

$$\int_a^b f(x)\phi_\nu(x)dx = \sum_{\mu=1}^{\infty} a_\mu \int_a^b \phi_\mu(x)\phi_\nu(x)dx = a_\nu,$$

† Here we are using the fact that when the convergence is uniform term-by-term integration is allowable. Cf. Meschkowski (3) VI or Hyslop, *Infinite Series*, p. 75.

that is,

$$a_\nu = (f,\phi_\nu), \qquad (\nu = 1, 2, 3, \ldots). \tag{4.6}$$

The coefficients a_ν are uniquely determined by this generalisation of the formulae for the Fourier coefficients.

It further follows from (4.5) that

$$\int_a^b \left(f - \sum_{\nu=1}^{\infty} a_\nu \phi_\nu(x)\right)^2 dx = 0.$$

Bearing in mind the orthogonal relation (4.4), we obtain from this the generalisation of Bessel's equation (3.12):

$$\sum_{\nu=1}^{\infty} a_\nu^2 = (f,f) = \int_a^b f^2 dx. \tag{4.7}$$

This relations holds for all functions $f(x)$ which can be represented as a uniformly convergent series (4.5) † by means of the system $\phi_\nu(x)$.

For an arbitrary continuous function $f(x)$ the series $\Sigma a_\nu \phi_\nu(x)$ with coefficients $a_\nu = (f,\phi_\nu)$ formed according to (4.6) does not necessarily converge. But in all cases the generalisation of Bessel's inequality holds:

$$\int_a^b \left\{f(x) - \sum_{\nu=1}^{n} a_\nu \phi_\nu(x)\right\}^2 dx \geqslant 0$$

for all integral n, from which we obtain (again using (4.4))

$$\sum_{\nu=1}^{n} a_\nu^2 \leqslant (f,f) = \int_a^b f(x)^2 dx. \tag{4.8}$$

The extremal property of the coefficients of the trigonometric system proved in § 2.1 also holds for arbitrary orthonormal systems, as can be seen by a slight variation in the method of proof employed there:

† The equation (4.7) also holds under more general conditions (cf. Chapter VII).

If a_ν, given by (4.6), *are the Fourier coefficients of the orthonormal system $\phi_\nu(x)$,*† *the integral*

$$J_n = \int_a^b \left\{ f(x) - \sum_{\nu=1}^{n} c_\nu \phi_\nu(x) \right\}^2 dx$$

is a minimum when the c_ν are replaced by the coefficients a_ν determined by (4.6).

The definition (4.2) of the scalar product can be generalised in several ways. We can for instance admit complex-valued functions $f(x)$ and $g(x)$ and define

$$(f,g) = \int_a^b f(x)\overline{g(x)}dx, \qquad (4.9)$$

where the bar over $g(x)$ denotes the complex conjugate. In this case we have instead of (4.8)

$$\sum_{n=1}^{\infty} |a_n|^2 \leqslant (f,f) = \int_a^b |f|^2 dx. \qquad (4.8')$$

We can also introduce a positive function $p(x)$, the so-called **weighting function**, and define the scalar product as

$$(f,g) = \int_a^b p(x)f(x)\overline{g(x)}dx, \quad p(x)>0. \qquad (4.9')$$

In all these cases the scalar product obeys certain simple rules of calculation, which may be established directly from the definition:

$$\begin{aligned} (\alpha f(x),\beta g(x)) &= \alpha\bar{\beta}(f(x),g(x)), \\ (\alpha f+\beta g,h) &= \alpha(f,h)+\beta(g,h), \\ (f,g) &= \overline{(g,f)}, \end{aligned} \qquad (4.10)$$

where α, β are arbitrary complex numbers.

The concept of orthonormal systems is not however restricted to classes of functions defined in real intervals.

† For general orthonormal systems the integrals determined by (4.6) are also known as " Fourier coefficients ".

Some further examples may be given of possible generalisations.

Let **D** be a domain of the complex plane bounded by n smooth curves $\mathbf{C}_\nu$ ($\mathbf{C} = \bigcup_{\nu=1}^{n} \mathbf{C}_\nu$), and let $f(z)$ and $g(z)$ be functions analytic † in $\mathbf{D} \cup \mathbf{C}$. We may then define a scalar product of the functions $f(z)$ and $g(z)$ as follows:

$$(f,g) = \iint_{\mathbf{D}} f(z)\overline{g(z)}dxdy, \qquad z = x+iy. \tag{4.11}$$

Alternatively we may use the integral round the boundary to define a scalar product ‡

$$[f,g] = \int_{\mathbf{C}} f(z)\overline{g(z)}ds. \tag{4.12}$$

We see at once that the rules (4.10) also hold for the scalar products defined in (4.11) and (4.12). Bessel's inequality holds in the generalised form

$$\sum_{\nu=1}^{\infty} |a_\nu|^2 \leqslant (f,f) \tag{4.8'}$$

for all orthonormal systems with the associated scalar product defined by (4.2), (4.9), (4.9′), (4.11) or (4.12).

§ 4.2. Examples of orthonormal systems

(A) The functions of the set $\phi_n(x)$ defined in the interval [0, 1] by

$$\phi_n(x) = \begin{cases} 0 & \text{for } x \text{ outside } (2^{-n-1};2^{-n}), \\ 2\sqrt{3}(x-2^{-n-1})2^{3(n+1)/2} & \\ & \text{for } 2^{-n-1} \leqslant x \leqslant \tfrac{1}{2}(2^{-n-1}+2^{-n}), \\ -2\sqrt{3}(x-2^{-n})2^{3(n+1)/2} & \\ & \text{for } \tfrac{1}{2}(2^{-n-1}+2^{-n}) \leqslant x \leqslant 2^{-n} \end{cases} \tag{4.13}$$

† These ideas can also be formulated under much more general conditions.

‡ To distinguish the scalar products defined by (4.11) and (4.12) we use square brackets in (4.12); s is arc length along the boundary.

can be represented by line-segments. The graph of $\phi_1(x)$ is shown in Fig. 9. These functions form an orthonormal system in the interval [0, 1] with respect to the scalar product

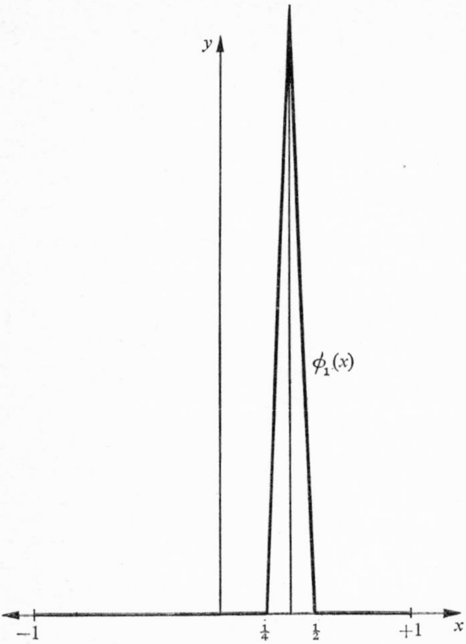

Fig. 9.

(4.2). The validity of the relation $(\phi_\nu,\phi_\mu) = 0$ for $\nu \neq \mu$ is immediately obvious if we observe that of the functions $\phi_\nu(x)$ and $\phi_\mu(x)$ at least one vanishes for every $x \in [0, 1]$. An elementary calculation shows that the normalisation condition

$$(\phi_\nu,\phi_\nu) = \int_0^1 \phi_\nu(x)^2 dx = 1$$

is also satisfied.

(B) To obtain an orthonormal system with a weighting function other than 1, consider the Chebyshev polynomials

$$T_0(x) = 1, \qquad T_n(x) = 2^{-n+1} \cos (n \text{ arc} \cos x), \qquad (4.14)$$

To see that the functions so defined are actually *polynomials*, we apply the well-known formula

$$\cos n\alpha = \cos^n \alpha - \binom{n}{2} \cos^{n-2} \alpha \sin^2 \alpha + \binom{n}{4} \cos^{n-4} \alpha \sin^4 \alpha - \dots$$

If we put $\cos \alpha = x$ in this equation, it follows that

$$\cos n\alpha = \cos (n \text{ arc} \cos x) = x^n - \binom{n}{2} x^{n-2}(1-x^2) + \binom{n}{4} x^{n-4}(1-x^2)^2 - \dots$$

Hence $T_n(x)$ is indeed a polynomial of degree n. That the polynomials of different orders are mutually orthogonal in the interval $[-1, 1]$ with a weighting function $(1-x^2)^{-\frac{1}{2}}$ can be shown by putting $x = \cos \alpha$, which gives

$$2\int_{-1}^{+1} \frac{T_\nu(x) T_\mu(x)}{\sqrt{(1-x^2)}} dx = \frac{1}{2^{\nu+\mu-2}} \int_0^{2\pi} \cos \nu\alpha \cos \mu\alpha d\alpha = 0$$

for $\nu \neq \mu$. The functions $T_n(x)$ are however not yet normalised in the interval $[-1, 1]$; for we have

$$\int_{-1}^{1} \frac{T_\nu^2(x)}{\sqrt{(1-x^2)}} dx = \frac{1}{2^{2\nu-1}} \int_0^{2\pi} \cos^2 \nu\alpha \, d\alpha = \frac{\pi}{2^{2\nu-1}},$$

from which it follows that the functions

$$\tau_n(x) = \frac{2^n}{\sqrt{(2\pi)}} T_n(x) \qquad (n = 1,2,3, \dots) \qquad (4.15)$$

form a *normalised* orthogonal system in the interval $[-1, 1]$, with the weighting function $(1-x^2)^{-\frac{1}{2}}$.

(C) The functions

$$\Phi_\nu(z) = \left(\frac{\nu}{\pi}\right)^{\frac{1}{2}} z^{\nu-1} \qquad (\nu = 1,2,3,\ldots) \qquad (4.16)$$

form an orthonormal system for the unit circle **U** in the complex plane, if the scalar product is defined by (4.11). For if we put $z = re^{i\phi}$, we obtain

$$\iint_{\mathbf{U}} \Phi_\nu(z)\overline{\Phi_\mu(z)}dxdy$$

$$= \frac{(\nu\mu)^{\frac{1}{2}}}{\pi}\int_{\phi=0}^{2\pi}\int_{r=0}^{1} e^{i\phi(\nu-\mu)}r^{\nu+\mu-1}drd\phi = \delta_{\nu\mu}.$$

The representation of functions in the form

$$f(z) = \sum_{\nu=1}^{\infty} a_\nu \Phi_\nu(z)$$

is therefore equivalent to representation by power series

$$f(z) = \sum_{\mu=0}^{\infty} b_\mu z^\mu, \qquad (4.17)$$

with $b_\mu = a_{\mu+1}(\mu+1)\ \pi^{-\frac{1}{2}}$.

In many investigations we are concerned with the class $\boldsymbol{H}$ of analytic functions for which the scalar product

$$(f,f) = \iint_{\mathbf{U}} |f|^2 dxdy = \sum_{\nu=1}^{\infty} |a_\nu|^2$$

is finite.† It is not identical with the set of functions regular in the unit circle. As is well-known (Hyslop, *Infinite Series*, p. 79) the radius of convergence of a power series is given by

$$(\overline{\lim}\ |b_n|^{1/n})^{-1}.$$

Hence the function

$$f(z) = \sum_{n=1}^{\infty} nz^n$$

† See Chapter VII.

is regular in the unit circle. But the integral

$$(f,f) = \iint_U |f|^2 dxdy$$

does not exist, since the series

$$\sum_{\nu=1}^{\infty} |a_\nu|^2 = \pi \sum_{\nu=2}^{\infty} \frac{(\nu-1)^2}{\nu}$$

is divergent.

(D) A further example of an orthonormal system may be given, in which the scalar product is defined by (4.12). For the circumference of the unit circle $|z| = 1$ in the complex plane

$$\chi_n(z) = (2\pi)^{-\frac{1}{2}} z^{n-1} \qquad (n = 1,2,3, \ldots)$$

is a sequence of orthogonal functions; for, as can readily be verified,

$$[\chi_n, \chi_m] = \int_{|z|=1} \chi_n(z)\overline{\chi_m(z)} ds = \delta_{nm}.$$

§ **4.3. Schmidt's orthogonalisation process.** Suppose the functions $u_\nu(x)$ ($\nu = 1,2,3 \ldots, n$) are defined in an interval $[a, b]$ of the real axis. They are said to be **linearly dependent** † if coefficients c_ν ($\nu = 1,2,3, \ldots, n$) exist, for which

$$c_1u_1(x) + c_2u_2(x) + \ldots + c_nu_n(x) = 0 \qquad (4.19)$$

(for $a \leqslant x \leqslant b$), and

$$\sum_{\nu=1}^{n} |c_\nu|^2 > 0. \qquad (4.19')$$

If no such set c_ν ($\nu = 1,2,3, \ldots, n$) exists, the functions $u_\nu(x)$ are said to be **linearly independent**. A sequence $u_\nu(x)$ ($\nu = 1,2,3, \ldots$) is said to be linearly independent if every finite subset of the sequence is linearly independent.

† The same terminology is customary for functions defined in a region of the complex plane.

It is possible, by means of a simple process due to Erhard Schmidt, to **orthogonalise** any linearly independent sequence $u_\nu(x)$. More precisely:

Let $u_\nu(x)$ be a sequence of linearly independent functions continuous in an interval $[a, b]$ of the real axis.† *Then an orthonormal system $v_\nu(x)$ exists, the functions of which can be written as linear combinations of the $u_\nu(x)$:*

$$\begin{aligned}
v_1(x) &= c_{11}u_1(x), \\
v_2(x) &= c_{21}u_1(x)+c_{22}u_2(x), \\
&\dots \\
v_n(x) &= c_{n1}u_1(x)+c_{n2}u_2(x)+ \dots +c_{nn}u_n(x). \\
&\dots
\end{aligned} \tag{4.20}$$

If we take the coefficient c_{11} to be $\| u_1(x) \|^{-1}$, then the norm of

$$v_1(x) = \frac{u_1(x)}{\| u_1(x) \|}$$

is in fact 1. The function $v_2^*(x) = u_2(x)-(u_2,v_1)v_1(x)$ is then orthogonal to $v_1(x)$; for

$$(v_2^*(x),v_1(x)) = (u_2,v_1)-(u_2,v_1) = 0. \tag{4.21}$$

$v_2^*(x)$ cannot vanish identically, since if it did, $u_2(x)$ and $v_1(x)$, and hence also $u_2(x)$ and $u_1(x)$ would be linearly dependent. Now the norm

$$\| v_2^*(x) \| = +\sqrt{\left\{\int_a^b (v_2^*(x))^2 dx\right\}}$$

of a continuous function which does not vanish identically is positive. We can therefore divide by $\| v_2^* \|$ and obtain

$$v_2(x) = \frac{v_2^*(x)}{\| v_2^* \|},$$

which is a normalised function orthogonal to $v_1(x)$.

† It is also possible to apply the process to sequences of functions defined in a region of the complex plane.

Let us now suppose that the functions of our system $v_n(x)$ have been determined up to and including the k-th. We then define

$$v^*_{k+1}(x) = u_{k+1}(x) - \sum_{\kappa=1}^{k} (u_{k+1}, v_\kappa) v_\kappa(x).$$

This function is again orthogonal to all $v_\kappa(x)$ with index $\kappa \leqslant k$. It cannot vanish identically, for if it did the functions

$$u_1(x), u_2(x), \ldots u_{k+1}(x),$$

being linear combinations of the $v_\kappa(x)$, would be linearly dependent. The function

$$v_{k+1}(x) = v^*_{k+1}(x) \parallel v^*_{k+1}(x) \parallel^{-1}$$

is accordingly normalised and orthogonal to all the functions $v_\kappa(x)$ $(\kappa = 1,2,3, \ldots, k)$.

This proof by induction shows that it is possible to associate with the sequence $u_n(x)$ a definite sequence of mutually orthogonal functions $v_n(x)$.

We also note that the coefficients c_{nn} in (4.20) obtained by this process are always non-zero, so that we can solve (4.20) for $u_1(x)$, $u_2(x) \ldots$ and obtain

$$\begin{aligned} u_1(x) &= d_{11} v_1(x), \\ u_2(x) &= d_{21} v_1(x) + d_{22} v_2(x), \\ &\ldots \\ u_n(x) &= d_{n1} v_1(x) + d_{n2} v_2(x) + \ldots + d_{nn} v_n(x), \\ &\ldots \end{aligned} \tag{4.20'}$$

If we apply Schmidt's process to the sequence of powers †

$$1, x, x^2, x^3, \ldots \tag{4.22}$$

† The linear independence of the sequence (4.22) follows immediately from the fact that the polynomial $\Sigma c_\nu x^\nu$ does not vanish identically for $\Sigma \mid c_\nu \mid^2 > 0$.

in the interval $[-1, 1]$, we obtain the functions †

$$v_0(x) = \tfrac{1}{2}\sqrt{2}, \qquad v_1(x) = \sqrt{\tfrac{3}{2}}x,$$
$$v_2(x) = \sqrt{\tfrac{5}{2}}(\tfrac{3}{2}x^2 - \tfrac{1}{2}), \qquad v_3(x) = \sqrt{\tfrac{7}{2}}(\tfrac{5}{2}x^3 - \tfrac{3}{2}x), \tag{4.23}$$
$$v_4(x) = \sqrt{\tfrac{9}{2}}(\tfrac{35}{8}x^4 - \tfrac{15}{4}x^2 + \tfrac{3}{8}), \ldots$$

as the first members of the sequence $v_n(x)$.

For subsequent applications we require a representation of the functions $v_n(x)$ by determinants. To obtain this we define

$$U_n(x) = \begin{vmatrix} (u_1,u_1) \ldots (u_1,u_{n-1}) \, u_1(x) \\ (u_2,u_1) \ldots (u_2,u_{n-1}) \, u_2(x) \\ \cdots\cdots\cdots\cdots\cdots \\ (u_n,u_1) \ldots (u_n,u_{n-1}) \, u_n(x) \end{vmatrix},$$

$$C_n = \begin{vmatrix} c_{11} & 0 & 0 \ldots 0 \\ c_{21} & c_{22} & 0 \ldots 0 \\ \cdots & \cdots & \cdots\cdots \\ c_{n1} & c_{n2} & c_{n3} \ldots c_{nn} \end{vmatrix},$$

where the $c_{\nu\mu}$ are the coefficients occurring in (4.20). If we form the product of these two determinants, combining rows of C_n with columns of U_n, we obtain, by (4.20),

$$C_n U_n(x) = \begin{vmatrix} (v_1,u_1) \ldots (v_1,u_{n-1}) \, v_1(x) \\ (v_2,u_1) \ldots (v_2,u_{n-1}) \, v_2(x) \\ \cdots\cdots\cdots\cdots\cdots \\ (v_n,u_1) \ldots (v_n,u_{n-1}) \, v_n(x) \end{vmatrix}.$$

We now border the determinant C_{n-1} and write

† It is convenient to start with the index 0; $v_n(x)$ is then a polynomial of degree n.

$$C_{n-1} = \begin{vmatrix} c_{11} & 0 & 0 \ldots & & 0 \\ c_{21} & c_{22} & 0 \ldots & & 0 \\ \cdot & \cdot & \cdot & \cdot & \cdot \\ c_{n-1,1} & c_{n-1,2} & \ldots & c_{n-1,n-1} & 0 \\ 0 & 0 & \ldots 0 & & 1 \end{vmatrix}.$$

and then multiply C_{n-1} by $C_n U_n(x)$ row by row. Since $(v_\nu, v_\mu) = \delta_{\nu\mu}$, the result is

$$C_n U_n(x) C_{n-1} = \begin{vmatrix} (v_1,v_1) \ldots (v_1,v_{n-1}) v_1(x) \\ \cdot \qquad\qquad \cdot \\ \cdot \qquad\qquad \cdot \\ \cdot \qquad\qquad \cdot \\ (v_n,v_1) \ldots (v_n,v_{n-1}) v_n(x) \end{vmatrix} = v_n(x).$$

Thus $v_n(x)$ has been expressed as a product of determinants

$$v_n(x) = C_n C_{n-1} U_n(x). \tag{4.24}$$

By a slight modification of this calculation we obtain for the so-called ' Gram's determinant ' of the functions $u_1(x)$, $u_2(x), \ldots u_n(x)$,

$$G = \begin{vmatrix} (u_1,u_1) \ldots (u_1,u_n) \\ \cdot \qquad\qquad \cdot \\ \cdot \qquad\qquad \cdot \\ \cdot \qquad\qquad \cdot \\ (u_n,u_1) \ldots (u_n,u_n) \end{vmatrix} \tag{4.25}$$

the relation

$$G C_n C_{n-1} = \det \{(v_i,v_k)\} = 1. \tag{4.26}$$

In carrying out Schmidt's orthogonalisation process we assumed the sequence $u_n(x)$ to be linearly independent. Formulae (4.26) now provides us with an important **criterion for linear independence.**

The continuous functions

$$u_1(x), u_2(x), \ldots, u_n(x) \tag{4.27}$$

are linearly independent if, and only if, their Gram's determinant (4.25) *does not vanish.*

For, if the functions (4.27) are linearly independent, they can be orthogonalised by Erhard Schmidt's process, and the relation (4.26) for the sequence $u_n(x)$ shows that G is non-zero. If, on the other hand, the functions (4.27) are linearly dependent, it follows from the relation

$$c_1 u_1(x) + c_2 u_2(x) + \ldots c_n u_n(x) = 0$$

that

$$\sum_{\nu=1}^{n} c_\nu (u_\nu, u_\mu) = 0, \qquad \mu = 1, 2, \ldots, n. \tag{4.28}$$

By (4.19′) the determinant G of this set of equations must vanish.

§ **4.4. The orthogonality of the Legendre polynomials.** We shall now investigate in greater detail the properties of some orthonormal systems which are of importance in applications. We begin with Legendre's polynomials, which are most simply defined by

$$P_0(x) = 1, \qquad P_n(x) = \frac{1}{2^n n!} \frac{d^n (x^2-1)^n}{dx^n}, \qquad n = 1, 2, 3, \ldots \tag{4.29}$$

If we write $(-1+x^2)^n$ in the form

$$(-1+x^2)^n = (-1)^n + (-1)^{n-1}\binom{n}{1}x^2 + \ldots$$
$$+ (-1)^{n-\nu}\binom{n}{\nu}x^{2\nu} + \ldots + x^{2n},$$

it follows that

$$P_n(x) = \frac{1}{2^n n!} \sum_{\nu=0}^{n}{}' (-1)^{n-\nu}\binom{n}{\nu}\frac{(2\nu)!}{(2\nu-n)!}x^{2\nu-n}.$$

In this expression the accented summation sign indicates that only those terms for which the exponent of x is non-negative are to be summed. To transform this further, we take the factor $(2^n n!)^{-1}$ inside the sign of summation and write

$$\frac{1}{2^n n!}\binom{n}{\nu}\frac{(2\nu)!}{(2\nu-n)!}=\frac{n!(2\nu)!}{2^n n!(n-\nu)!\nu!(2\nu-n)!}$$

$$=\frac{(2\nu)!}{(n-\nu)!(2\nu-n)!\nu!2^n 2^{-\nu}2^\nu}$$

$$=\frac{1}{2^{n-\nu}(n-\nu)!(2\nu-n)!}\frac{(2\nu)!}{\nu!2^\nu}.$$

The last fraction can be transformed as follows :

$$\frac{(2\nu)!}{\nu!2^\nu}=1.3.5\ldots(2\nu-1).$$

Hence $P_n(x)$ becomes

$$P_n(x)=\sum_{\nu=0}^{n}{}'(-1)^{n-\nu}\frac{1.3.5\ldots(2\nu-1)}{(n-\nu)!(2\nu-n)!2^{n-\nu}}x^{2\nu-n}, \quad (4.30)$$

and we have

$$\begin{aligned}&P_0(x)=1, && P_1(x)=x, && P_2(x)=\tfrac{3}{2}x^2-\tfrac{1}{2},\\ &P_3(x)=\tfrac{5}{2}x^3-\tfrac{3}{2}x, && P_4(x)=\tfrac{35}{8}x^4-\tfrac{15}{4}x^2+\tfrac{3}{8},\ldots\end{aligned} \quad (4.31)$$

We now demonstrate the orthogonality of this system. For this purpose we put

$$(x^2-1)^n=\rho_n(x).$$

Then

$$\int_{-1}^{1}P_n(x)x^m dx=\frac{1}{2^n n!}\int_{-1}^{1}\rho_n^{(n)}(x)x^m dx. \quad (4.32)$$

This integral will be evaluated for $m<n$ by recursion. We note that

$$\rho_n^{(\nu)}(x)=0$$

for $x = \pm 1$ and $\nu = 0, 1, 2, \ldots, (n-1)$. Hence by integration by parts (4.32) becomes

$$\int_{-1}^{1} \rho_n^{(n)}(x) x^m dx = -m \int_{-1}^{1} \rho_n^{(n-1)}(x) x^{m-1} dx.$$

Repetition of this operation ultimately leads to

$$m!(-1)^m \int_{-1}^{1} \rho_n^{(n-m)}(x) dx = m!(-1)^m [\rho_n^{(n-m-1)}(x)]_{-1}^{1} = 0$$

for $m<n$.

Accordingly,

$$\int_{-1}^{1} P_n(x) x^m dx = 0 \tag{4.33}$$

for $m<n$. Since $P_m(x)$ is a polynomial of degree m, we also have

$$\int_{-1}^{1} P_n(x) P_m(x) dx = 0. \tag{4.33'}$$

This establishes the orthogonality of the Legendre polynomials $P_n(x)$. To obtain an *orthonormal* system from the Legendre polynomials we evaluate

$$J = \int_{-1}^{1} \{P_n(x)\}^2 dx.$$

By repeated integration by parts we obtain first

$$\begin{aligned} \int_{-1}^{1} (1-x^2)^n dx &= \int_{-1}^{1} (1-x)^n (1+x)^n dx \\ &= \frac{n}{n+1} \int_{-1}^{1} (1-x)^{n-1} (1+x)^{n+1} dx = \ldots \\ &= \frac{n(n-1)\ldots 2 \, . \, 1}{(n+1)(n+2)\ldots 2n} \int_{-1}^{1} (1+x)^{2n} dx \\ &= \frac{(n!)^2}{(2n)!} \frac{2^{2n+1}}{2n+1}, \end{aligned} \tag{4.34}$$

and further, again by integration by parts,

$$\int_{-1}^{1} \{\rho_n^{(n)}(x)\}^2 dx = 0 - \int_{-1}^{1} \rho_n^{(n-1)}(x)\rho_n^{(n+1)}(x)dx = \dots$$

$$= (-1)^n \int_{-1}^{1} \rho_n(x)\rho_n^{(2n)}(x)dx = (2n)! \int_{-1}^{1} (1-x)^n(1+x)^n dx. \tag{4.35}$$

Here we have used the fact that the $2n$-th derivative of $\rho_n(x) = (x^2-1)^n$ is the same as the derivative of the term of exponent $2n$. The $2n$-th derivatives of all the other terms of the sum vanish.

Thus by (4.29), (4.35) and (4.34), we have

$$\int_{-1}^{1} \{P_n(x)\}^2 dx = \frac{1}{(2^n n!)^2}(2n)! \frac{(n!)^2 2^{2n+1}}{(2n)!(2n+1)} = \frac{2}{2n+1}.$$

Accordingly the polynomials

$$P_n^*(x) = \sqrt{\left(\frac{2n+1}{2}\right)} P_n(x) = \sqrt{\left(\frac{2n+1}{2}\right)} \frac{1}{2^n n!} \frac{d^n(x^2-1)^n}{dx^n},$$

$$n = 0,1,2,\dots \tag{4.36}$$

form an orthonormal system. The function of index n is a polynomial of degree n. The system (4.36) is identical with the system (4.23) arising by orthogonalisation of powers (4.22). This can readily be established from the uniqueness of Schmidt's process.

The Legendre polynomials are characterised by a remarkable extremal property. To formulate this conveniently, we introduce the polynomials

$$\hat{P}_n(x) = \frac{1}{c_n} P_n(x),$$

where c_n is the coefficient of the term with exponent n; $\hat{P}_n(x)$ is accordingly a polynomial of degree n, with 1 as the coefficient of x^n. Then the following result holds:

Of all the polynomials

$$p_n(x) = x^n + a_{n-1}x^{n-1} + \ldots + a_1 x + a_0$$

$\hat{P}_n(x)$ *has the smallest norm; that is to say:*

$$\| p_n(x) \|^2 = (p_n, p_n) \geqq (\hat{P}_n, \hat{P}_n) = \| \hat{P}_n(x) \|^2 = \int_{-1}^{1} \hat{P}_n(x)^2 dx. \tag{4.37}$$

To prove (4.37) we write the scalar product (p_n, p_n) as follows:

$$(p_n, p_n) = (p_n - \hat{P}_n + \hat{P}_n, p_n - \hat{P}_n + \hat{P}_n) = (q_{n-1} + \hat{P}_n, q_{n-1} + \hat{P}_n),$$

where q_{n-1} has been written for $p_n - \hat{P}_n$. We then have, by the rule (4.9),

$$(p_n, p_n) = (q_{n-1}, q_{n-1}) + (q_{n-1}, \hat{P}_n) + (\hat{P}_n, q_{n-1}) + (\hat{P}_n, \hat{P}_n).$$

But

$$(q_{n-1}, \hat{P}_n) = (\hat{P}_n, q_{n-1}) = 0,$$

since $q_{n-1} = p_n - \hat{P}_n$ is a polynomial of degree $n-1$. This is an immediate consequence of (4.33). We therefore have the result

$$(p_n, p_n) = (q_{n-1}, q_{n-1}) + (\hat{P}_n, \hat{P}_n) \geqslant (\hat{P}_n, \hat{P}_n). \tag{4.38}$$

§4.5. A recurrence relation for $P_n(x)$. A different approach to the Legendre polynomials is by way of a physical problem:

Suppose a gravitating particle of unit mass situated at the north pole N of the unit sphere; let it attract a second particle of unit mass situated at a point P inside the sphere, distant r from its centre C. (Fig. 10). *Let α be the angle between the vectors CN and CP. It is required to find the potential $h(r,\alpha)$ of the gravitational field of the first particle.*

As is well known, this potential is given by $(PN)^{-1}$, and has the value

$$h(r,\alpha) = H(r,x) = \frac{1}{\sqrt{(1-2rx+r^2)}}, \tag{4.39}$$

where x denotes $\cos\alpha$. Let us expand this function as a power series in r:

$$\frac{1}{\sqrt{(1-2rx+r^2)}} = \sum_{n=0}^{\infty} l_n(x)r^n. \tag{4.40}$$

By Taylor's Theorem the coefficients $l_n(x)$ are given by

$$l_n(x) = \frac{1}{n!}\left[\frac{d^n H(r,x)}{dx^n}\right]_{r=0}. \tag{4.41}$$

In this way we obtain

$$l_0(x) = 1,\ l_1(x) = x,\ l_2(x) = \tfrac{1}{2}(3x^2-1),\ l_3(x) = \tfrac{1}{2}(5x^3-3x). \tag{4.42}$$

These functions are in fact the same as the first four functions of the sequence $P_n(x)$. We shall show that $l_n(x) = P_n(x)$ for all n.

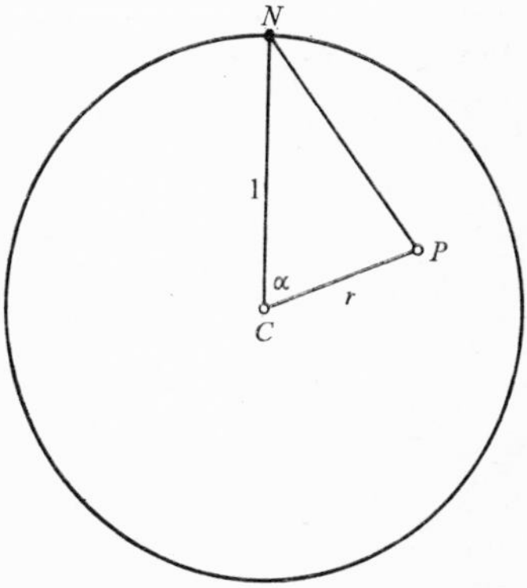

Fig. 10.

With a view to this we first obtain a recurrence relation, which facilitates the calculation of the functions $l_n(x)$.

Differentiating both sides of equation (4.40) with respect

to r, we obtain

$$\frac{x-r}{(1-2rx+r^2)^{\frac{3}{2}}} = \sum_{n=0}^{\infty} l_n(x) n r^{n-1}. \qquad (4.43)$$

Multiplication of both sides of the equation (4.43) by $(1-2rx+r^2)$ gives

$$\frac{x-r}{(1-2rx+r^2)^{\frac{1}{2}}} = (1-2rx+r^2)\sum_{n=0}^{\infty} l_n(x) n r^{n-1}. \qquad (4.44)$$

But by (4.40),

$$\frac{x-r}{(1-2rx+r^2)^{\frac{1}{2}}} = (x-r)\sum_{n=0}^{\infty} l_n(x) r^n. \qquad (4.45)$$

It then follows from (4.44) and (4.45) that

$$\sum_{n=0}^{\infty} [nr^{n-1} - 2xnr^n + nr^{n+1}] l_n(x) = \sum_{n=0}^{\infty} [xr^n - r^{n+1}] l_n(x). \qquad (4.46)$$

The coefficients of r^n (for all $n \geqslant 1$) must be equal on the two sides of (4.46), which leads to the required recurrence relation for the functions $l_n(x)$. For all $n \geqslant 1$ we have

$$(n+1) l_{n+1}(x) = x(1+2n) l_n(x) - n l_{n-1}(x). \qquad (4.47)$$

We immediately see from (4.42) and (4.47) that the functions $l_n(x)$ are polynomials of degree n. If we can also show that the functions

$$l_n^*(x) = \sqrt{\left(\frac{2n+1}{2}\right)} l_n(x) \qquad (n = 0,1,2,\ldots) \qquad (4.48)$$

form an orthonormal system, the identity of the functions with the Legendre polynomials will be assured; for the functions $l_n^*(x)$ and $P_n^*(x)$ are the uniquely determined orthonormal functions belonging to the system of powers x^n $(n = 0,1,2,3,\ldots)$.

To prove the orthogonality of the system (4.48) we multiply equation (4.40) by a corresponding equation for

$\rho < 1$ (in place of $r < 1$). This gives

$$(1-2xr+r^2)^{-\frac{1}{2}}(1-2x\rho+\rho^2)^{-\frac{1}{2}} = \sum_{n,m=0}^{\infty} l_n(x)l_m(x)r^n\rho^m. \quad (4.49)$$

Integrating the left-hand side of this equation with respect to x from -1 to 1, we obtain

$$J(r,\rho) = \int_{-1}^{1} \frac{dx}{\sqrt{\{(1-2rx+r^2)(1-2\rho x+\rho^2)\}}}$$

$$= \frac{1}{\sqrt{(r\rho)}} \ln \frac{1+\sqrt{(r\rho)}}{1-\sqrt{(r\rho)}}.$$

If we expand $\ln (1+\sqrt{(r\rho)}) - \ln (1-\sqrt{(r\rho)})$ in a series, we find

$$J(r,\rho) = \sum_{n=0}^{\infty} \frac{2}{2n+1} r^n\rho^n. \quad (4.50)$$

We now integrate the right-hand side of (4.49) in the same way, using (4.50), and obtain the equation

$$\sum_{n,m=0}^{\infty} \left[\int_{-1}^{1} l_n(x)l_m(x)dx\right] r^n\rho^m = \sum_{n=0}^{\infty} \frac{2}{2n+1} r^n\rho^n.$$

Comparing coefficients we have

$$\int_{-1}^{1} l_n(x)l_m(x)dx = \begin{cases} 0 & \text{for } n \neq m, \\ \dfrac{2}{2n+1} & \text{for } n = m. \end{cases}$$

We have thus shown that the functions $\sqrt{\left(\frac{2n+1}{2}\right)} l_n(x) = l_n^*(x)$ do in fact form an orthonormal system. The identity of $l_n(x)$ and $P_n(x)$ is assured, and we may write (4.47) as a recurrence relation for the Legendre polynomials defined by (4.29)

$$(n+1)P_{n+1}(x) = x(1+2n)P_n(x) - nP_{n-1}(x),$$

$$n = 1,2,3, \ldots \quad (4.47')$$

Finally we note the differential equation of the Legendre polynomials

$$(x^2-1)y''+2xy'-n(n+1)y=0 \tag{4.51}$$

which can readily be derived from the defining equation (4.29). The proof is left to the reader.

§ **4.6. Orthonormal systems for infinite intervals.** We may define a scalar product for the interval $(-\infty,+\infty)$ using the weighting function e^{-x^2}:

$$(f,g)_H = \int_{-\infty}^{\infty} e^{-x^2} f(x)g(x)dx. \tag{4.52}$$

For this scalar product the Hermite polynomials †

$$H_n(x) = (-1)^n e^{x^2} \frac{d^n e^{-x^2}}{dx^n} \qquad (n=0,1,2,\ldots) \quad (4.53$$

form an orthogonal system. We readily see that the functions so defined are polynomials; we have

$H_0(x)=1$, $H_1(x)=2x$, $H_2(x)=4x^2-2$, $H_3(x)=8x^3-12x$, $H_4(x)=16x^4-48x^2+12, \ldots$

Proceeding in this way from n to $n+1$ we see that the functions $H_n(x)$ are all polynomials of degree n.

To prove their orthogonality we integrate

$$(H_n,H_m)_H = (-1)^{n+m}\int_{-\infty}^{\infty} e^{x^2}\frac{d^n e^{-x^2}}{dx^n}\frac{d^m e^{-x^2}}{dx^m}dx$$

by parts. Then

$$(-1)^{n+m}(H_n,H_m)_H = \left[e^{x^2}\frac{d^n e^{-x^2}}{dx^n}\frac{d^{m-1}e^{-x^2}}{dx^{m-1}}\right]_{\infty}^{-\infty} -$$

$$\int_{-\infty}^{\infty}\frac{d}{dx}\left[e^{x^2}\frac{d^n e^{-x^2}}{dx^n}\right]\frac{d^{m-1}e^{-x^2}}{dx^{m-1}}dx. \tag{4.54}$$

† So named after Charles Hermite (1822-1901).

Now all terms in

$$\frac{d^n e^{-x^2}}{dx^n} \text{ and } \frac{d^{m-1} e^{-x^2}}{dx^{m-1}}$$

contain the factor e^{-x^2}. Since

$$\lim_{x\to\infty} x^k e^{-x^2} = 0,$$

the first term on the right of (4.54) vanishes. Repeated integration by parts therefore leads to

$$(H_n,H_m)_H = 0 \qquad (4.55)$$

for $n \neq m$. The details of this proof, and the calculation of $(H_n,H_n)_H$ are left to the reader. The result is

$$(H_n,H_n)_H = \int_{-\infty}^{\infty} H_n^2(x)e^{-x^2}dx = 2^n n!\sqrt{\pi},$$

so that the functions

$$H_n^*(x) = (2^n n!\sqrt{\pi})^{-\frac{1}{2}} H_n(x) \qquad (4.56)$$

form a *normalised* orthogonal system for the interval $(-\infty,\infty)$ with the weighting function e^{-x^2}.

From the definition of the Hermite polynomials we readily obtain the recurrence relation

$$H_{n+1}(x) - 2xH_n(x) + 2nH_{n-1}(x) = 0 \qquad (n \geqslant 1) \ (4.57)$$

and the differential equation

$$\frac{d^2y}{dx^2} - 2x\frac{dy}{dx} + 2ny = 0 \qquad (n = 0,1,2,\ldots). \qquad (4.58)$$

For the interval $(0,\infty)$ and the scalar product

$$(f,g)_\lambda = \int_0^\infty e^{-x} f(x)g(x)dx \qquad (4.59)$$

the Laguerre polynomials

$$\lambda_n(x) = e^x \frac{d^n(x^n e^{-x})}{dx^n} \qquad (4.60)$$

form a system of (un-normalised) orthogonal functions. In this case we have

$$\int_0^\infty e^{-x}\lambda_n(x)\lambda_m(x)dx = \begin{cases} 0 & \text{for } n \neq m, \\ (n!)^2 & \text{for } n = m. \end{cases} \qquad (4.55')$$

The proof is, as before, by repeated integration by parts. The functions

$$\lambda_n^*(x) = \frac{1}{n!}\lambda_n(x) \qquad (n = 0,1,2,3,\ldots) \qquad (4.56')$$

therefore form an orthonormal system for the interval $(0,\infty)$ and the weighting function e^{-x}. Alternatively we can of course say that the functions

$$\frac{1}{n!}e^{-x/2}\lambda_n(x)$$

form an orthonormal system for the interval $(0,\infty)$ with unity as weighting function.

The Laguerre polynomials † satisfy the following recurrence relation, which may readily be derived from the defining equation

$$\lambda_{n+1}(x)-(2n+1-x)\lambda_n(x)+n^2\lambda_{n-1}(x) = 0 \qquad (n = 1,2,3,\ldots) \qquad (4.57')$$

and the differential equation

$$x\frac{d^2y}{dx^2}+(1-x)\frac{dy}{dx}+ny = 0. \qquad (4.58')$$

§ 4.7. Exercises

1. Show that

$$\frac{1}{\sqrt{\pi}}, \sqrt{\left(\frac{2}{\pi}\right)}\cos x, \sqrt{\left(\frac{2}{\pi}\right)}\cos 2x, \ldots$$

is an orthonormal system in the interval $[0, \pi]$.

† Other examples of notable orthogonal systems may be found, e.g. in Schmeidler, *Linear Operators in Hilbert Space*, or Tricomi, *Vorlesungen über Orthogonalreihen.*

2. Show that

$$\frac{2}{\sqrt{\pi}}\sin x,\ \frac{2}{\sqrt{\pi}}\sin 3x,\ \frac{2}{\sqrt{\pi}}\sin 5x, \ldots$$

is an orthonormal system in the interval $[0, \frac{1}{2}\pi]$.

3. The values of x in the interval $[0, 1]$ expressed in the binary scale are

$$x = 2^{-1}a_1(x)+2^{-2}a_2(x)+2^{-3}a_3(x)+ \ldots,$$

where $a_\nu(x) = 1$ or 0. (This number may be written in analogy with ordinary decimal notation, but with a semicolon in place of the decimal point, thus: $0; a_1a_2a_3\ldots$). Consider the system of functions defined in the interval $[0, 1]$ by

$$\phi_\nu(x) = \begin{cases} +1 \text{ if } a_\nu(x) = 0 \\ -1 \text{ if } a_\nu(x) = 1. \end{cases}$$

Show that this system (given by Rademacher) is orthogonal in the interval $[0, 1]$, with weighting function 1.

4. Show that any sequence of orthogonal functions is linearly independent.

5. Calculate the first three terms in the expansion of e^x in the interval $(-1, 1)$ in terms of the orthonormal system of the Legendre polynomials.

6. Expand $f(x) = \operatorname{sgn} x = x/|x|$ in the interval $(-1, 1)$ in terms of Legendre polynomials.

7. Show, that for any polynomial of degree n of the form

$$p_n(x) = x^n + a_{n-1}x^{n-1} + \ldots + a_0,$$

$$\operatorname{Max} | p_n(x) | \geqslant \operatorname{Max} | T_n(x) |,$$

where $T_n(x)$ denotes the n-th Chebyshev polynomial.

CHAPTER V

COMPLETENESS OF SYSTEMS OF FUNCTIONS

§ **5.1. Approximation in mean.** Let C be the class of functions continuous in a closed interval $[a, b]$ of the real axis, and let $\phi_\nu(x)$ be a sequence of continuous functions orthogonal in $[a, b]$. The sequence $\phi_\nu(x)$ is said to be **complete** with respect to C if for every positive ε and for every function $f(x) \in C$ a linear combination

$$l(x) = \sum_{\nu=1}^{n} c_\nu \phi_\nu(x) \tag{5.1}$$

exists such that †

$$\| f(x) - l(x) \| = +\sqrt{\left\{\int_a^b | f(x) - l(x) |^2 dx\right\}} < \varepsilon. \tag{5.2}$$

We may express this otherwise by the statement that every function $f(x) \in C$ can be approximated arbitrarily closely ' in mean ' by a linear combination of the type (5.1).

A sequence

$$l_n(x) = \sum_{\nu=1}^{n} a_\nu^{(n)} \phi_\nu(x) \tag{5.1'}$$

is said to **converge in mean** to the function $f(x)$ if for every $\varepsilon > 0$ a number N exists such that for all $n > N$

$$\| f(x) - l_n(x) \| < \varepsilon \tag{5.2'}$$

for every $f(x) \in C$.

This convergence in mean is to be clearly distinguished from ordinary ' pointwise ' convergence and from uniform convergence. Let us suppose that a sequence (5.1') converges uniformly in $[a, b]$ to a limiting function $f(x) \in C$.

† The definition of completeness can be suitably modified for the scalar products defined by (4.9'), (4.11) or (4.12).

This means that for arbitrarily given $\eta>0$ and sufficiently large n, independent of x,

$$|f(x)-l_n(x)|<\eta. \tag{5.3}$$

It immediately follows that

$$\| f(x)-l_n(x) \| <\eta\sqrt{(b-a)},$$

i.e.,

$$\| f(x)-l_n(x) \| <\varepsilon$$

for $\varepsilon = \eta\sqrt{(b-a)}$. Hence uniform convergence implies mean convergence. We shall show later that the converse of this statement does not hold.

By the results of § 2.1 and § 4.1 we obtain the best approximation in mean using linear combinations of type (5.1) if we replace the coefficients c_ν in (5.1) by the Fourier coefficients

$$a_\nu = (f,\phi_\nu) = \int_a^b f(x)\overline{\phi_\nu(x)}dx. \tag{5.4}$$

Our system $\phi_\nu(x)$ is therefore complete with respect to $\boldsymbol{C}$ if and only if, for arbitrarily given ε and sufficiently large n,

$$\left(f-\sum_{\nu=1}^{n} a_\nu\phi_\nu(x),\, f-\sum_{\nu=1}^{n} a_\nu\phi_\nu(x)\right)<\varepsilon.$$

In this case we have

$$\lim_{n\to\infty}\sum_{\nu=1}^{n} |a_\nu|^2 = (f,f).$$

Hence the necessary and sufficient condition for the completeness of the system $\phi_\nu(x)$ with respect to $\boldsymbol{C}$ is that Bessel's equation

$$(f,f)= \sum_{\nu=1}^{\infty} |a_\nu|^2 \tag{5.5}$$

should hold for all functions $f(x)\in\boldsymbol{C}$. On this account the equation (5.5) is known as the **completeness relation.**

In § 2.2 we introduced the notation $\sim$ for the correspondence between a function $f(x)$ and its Fourier series formally constructed, without regard to convergence or divergence. For arbitrary orthonormal systems we may write in the same way

$$f(x) \sim \sum_{\nu=1}^{\infty} a_\nu \phi_\nu(x), \qquad a_\nu = (f, \phi_\nu), \qquad \nu = 1,2,3,\ldots \tag{5.6}$$

We shall now adopt the convention † that

$$f(x) \approx \sum_{\nu=1}^{\infty} a_\nu \phi_\nu(x) \tag{5.7}$$

stands for convergence in mean. Then (5.7) means that for every $\varepsilon > 0$ a number $N(\varepsilon)$ exists such that

$$\| f(x) - \sum_{\nu=1}^{n} a_\nu \phi_\nu(x) \| < \varepsilon \tag{5.7$'$}$$

for $n > N(\varepsilon)$. On the other hand the equation

$$f(x) = \sum_{\nu=1}^{\infty} a_\nu \phi_\nu(x) \tag{5.8}$$

means that for sufficiently large n ($n > N(\varepsilon, x)$),

$$\left| f(x) - \sum_{\nu=1}^{n} a_\nu \phi_\nu(x) \right| < \varepsilon\,. \tag{5.8$'$}$$

If the inequality (5.8′) holds for all $n > N^*(\varepsilon)$, *uniformly in x*, that is, if (5.8) converges uniformly in $[a, b]$, the weaker statements (5.7) and (5.7′) also hold.

§ **5.2. Weierstrass's approximation theorem.** We shall now establish the completeness of some important orthonormal systems. We begin with a fundamental theorem due to Weierstrass.

For every $\varepsilon > 0$ *and for every function* $f(x) \in C$ *a polynomial* $p_n(x)$ *of degree* $2n$ *exists, such that for sufficiently large n*

$$| f(x) - p_n(x) | < \varepsilon \tag{5.9}$$

for all $x \in [a, b]$.

† The symbol $\approx$ is read " is equivalent to ".

To prove this theorem we confine ourselves in the first place to the interval [0, 1] and find a lower bound for the integral †

$$J_n = \int_0^1 (1-v^2)^n dv.$$

We have

$$J_n = \int_0^1 (1+v)^n (1-v)^n dv > \int_0^1 (1-v)^n dv$$
$$= -\frac{1}{n+1}[(1-v)^{n+1}]_0^1 = \frac{1}{n+1}. \tag{5.10}$$

Now let

$$J_n(\delta) = \int_\delta^1 (1-v^2)^n dv$$

for $0<\delta<1$. Then $1-v^2 \leqslant 1-\delta^2$, so that

$$J_n(\delta) < (1-\delta^2)^n (1-\delta) < (1-\delta^2)^n. \tag{5.11}$$

Finally (5.10) and (5.11) give

$$\frac{J_n(\delta)}{J_n} < (1-\delta^2)^n (n+1).$$

If we put

$$(1-\delta^2)^{-1} = \beta > 1,$$

we have

$$\frac{J_n(\delta)}{J_n} < \frac{n+1}{\beta^n}, \qquad \lim_{n\to\infty} \frac{J_n(\delta)}{J_n} = 0. \tag{5.12}$$

After these preliminaries we now define the polynomial that will be used to approximate the given continuous function $f(x)$ in the interval [0, 1]:

$$p_n(x) = \frac{\int_0^1 f(u)\{1-(u-x)^2\}^n du}{\int_{-1}^1 (1-u^2)^n du}, \qquad n = 1,2,3,\ldots \tag{5.13}$$

† Cf. equation (4.34).

We see immediately that the function $p_n(x)$ so defined is a polynomial of degree $2n$ in x. By means of the transformation $u = v+x$ we can transform the numerator $Z(x)$ of $p_n(x)$ into the form

$$Z(x) = \int_{-x}^{1-x} f(v+x)(1-v^2)^n dv = \int_{-x}^{-\delta} + \int_{-\delta}^{\delta} + \int_{\delta}^{1-x}$$

$$= I_1(x)+I_2(x)+I_3(x). \tag{5.14}$$

The integral $I_2(x)$ can be written in the alternative form

$$I_2(x) = f(x)\int_{-\delta}^{\delta} (1-v^2)^n dv + \int_{-\delta}^{\delta} \{f(v+x)-f(x)\}(1-v^2)^n dv. \tag{5.15}$$

We now make use of the continuity of the function $f(x)$ to be approximated, which we have assumed. For arbitrarily given ε, v can be chosen so small that $|f(v+x)-f(x)| < \varepsilon$. In the integral I_2, v varies between $-\delta$ and $+\delta$. Hence for δ sufficiently small we certainly have

$$|f(v+x)-f(x)| < \varepsilon \tag{5.16}$$

for all values v in the range of integration $[-\delta, \delta]$. We also have

$$\int_{-\delta}^{\delta} (1-v^2)^n dv = 2\int_{0}^{\delta} (1-v^2)^n dv = 2\{J_n - J_n(\delta)\},$$

so that (5.15) and (5.16) lead to

$$I_2(x) = 2f(x)\{J_n - J_n(\delta)\} + 2\langle\varepsilon\rangle J_n, \tag{5.17}$$

where $\langle\varepsilon\rangle$ denotes a positive or negative number whose absolute value is at most equal to ε.

Let M be the maximum of the continuous function $f(x)$ in the interval $[0, 1]$. We can then find the following upper bounds for the integrals I_1 and I_3 in (5.14):

$$\left. \begin{aligned} |I_1| &\leqslant M\int_{-1}^{-\delta}(1-v^2)^n dv = MJ_n(\delta), \\ |I_3| &\leqslant M\int_{\delta}^{1}(1-v^2)^n dv = MJ_n(\delta). \end{aligned} \right\} \tag{5.18}$$

Now the denominator in (5.13) is equal to $2J_n$. Hence (5.14) and (5.17) give

$$p_n(x)-f(x) = \{I_1(x)+I_3(x)+2\langle\varepsilon\rangle J_n - 2f(x)J_n(\delta)\}/2J_n,$$

and by (5.18) we obtain from this the upper bound

$$|p_n(x)-f(x)| < 2M\frac{J_n(\delta)}{J_n}+\varepsilon. \tag{5.19}$$

The right-hand side of (5.19) can be made less than any given positive number η. For this purpose we first choose δ so small that ε is less then $\frac{1}{2}\eta$, and afterwards choose n. By (5.12) we have, if n is sufficiently large,

$$\frac{J_n(\delta)}{J_n} < \frac{\eta}{4M}.$$

But this means that

$$|p_n(x)-f(x)| < \eta$$

for $n > N(\eta)$, i.e. the sequence of polynomials (5.13) converges uniformly in the interval $[0, 1]$ to the function $f(x)$.

It is clearly possible, by a suitable transformation of variables, to extend this result to any interval $[a, b]$ of the real axis. This completes the proof of Weierstrass's theorem.

§ 5.3. The completeness of Legendre's polynomials and of the trigonometric polynomials. In accordance with the remarks made in § 5.1, it follows from Weirstrass's theorem that any function continuous in an interval $[-1, 1]$ can also be approximated in mean by polynomials $p_n(x)$. We have

$$\| f(x)-p_n(x)\| = \left\{\int_{-1}^{1}|f(x)-p_n(x)|^2 dx\right\}^{\frac{1}{2}} < \varepsilon \tag{5.20}$$

for sufficiently large values of n. From this we can readily deduce that the Legendre polynomials are complete with respect to **C**. For the polynomials given by (4.36) can be obtained from the powers

$$1, x, x^2, x^3, \ldots$$

by Schmidt's process of orthogonalisation. We then have (cf. § 4.20):

$$\begin{aligned}\lambda_0(x) &= c_{11} \,.\, 1\\ \lambda_1(x) &= c_{21} \,.\, 1 + c_{22}x\\ \lambda_2(x) &= c_{31} \,.\, 1 + c_{32}x + c_{33}x^2\\ &\ldots\ldots\end{aligned}$$

This system can easily be solved for $1, x, x^2, x^3, \ldots$; let the solution be (cf. (4.20′)):

$$\begin{aligned}1 &= d_{11}\lambda_0(x)\\ x &= d_{21}\lambda_0(x) + d_{22}\lambda_1(x)\\ x^2 &= d_{31}\lambda_0(x) + d_{32}\lambda_1(x) + d_{33}\lambda_2(x)\\ &\ldots\ldots\end{aligned}$$

Thus any power and therefore also any polynomial $p_n(x)$ can be expressed as a linear combination of a finite number of Legendre polynomials. If the polynomial in (5.20) is of degree $2n$, we can also write this inequality in the form

$$\| f(x) - \sum_{\nu=0}^{2n} c_\nu \lambda_\nu(x) \| < \varepsilon. \tag{5.20′}$$

According to our theorem on approximation by orthonormal systems (p. 56) it follows from this that *a fortiori*

$$\| f(x) - \sum_{\nu=0}^{2n} a_\nu \lambda_\nu(x) \| < \varepsilon, \tag{5.21′}$$

where the a_ν are the Fourier coefficients of the given function $f(x)$ expanded in terms of the Legendre polynomials. This proves the completeness of the system (4.36).

The question of the completeness of the systems

$$\begin{matrix} \frac{1}{\sqrt{(2\pi)}}, & \frac{1}{\sqrt{\pi}}\cos x, & \frac{1}{\sqrt{\pi}}\cos 2x, & \frac{1}{\sqrt{\pi}}\cos 3x, \dots \\ & \frac{1}{\sqrt{\pi}}\sin x, & \frac{1}{\sqrt{\pi}}\sin 2x, & \frac{1}{\sqrt{\pi}}\sin 3x, \dots \end{matrix} \tag{5.22}$$

in the interval $[-\pi, \pi]$, with respect to functions continuous in this interval, can easily be reduced to that of the completeness of the powers x^n ($n = 0,1,2,3, \dots$) in the interval $[0, 1]$. It is however not difficult to give a direct proof. To

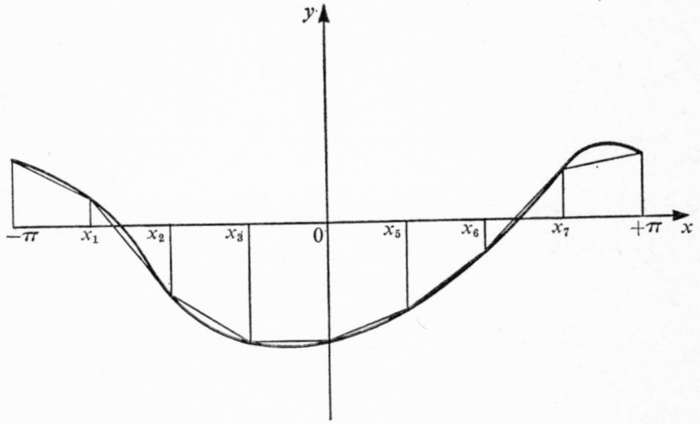

Fig. 11.

this end we first approximate the given continuous function $f(x)$ by a succession of straight-line segments $g_n(x)$ (Fig. 11).

If we divide the interval $[-\pi, \pi]$ into n sub-intervals of length $2\pi n^{-1}$, the points of division being $x_0, x_1, \dots, x_n$ ($x_0 = -\pi$, $x_n = \pi$), and define $g_n(x)$ in the interval $[x_\kappa, x_{\kappa+1}]$ by the equation

$$g_n(x) = \frac{f(x_{\kappa+1}) - f(x_\kappa)}{x_{\kappa+1} - x_\kappa}(x - x_\kappa) + f(x_\kappa), \qquad x_\kappa \leqslant x \leqslant x_{\kappa+1},$$

we have, because of the continuity of $f(x)$ that for arbitrary positive ε and sufficiently large n

$$|f(x)-g_n(x)|<\tfrac{1}{2}\varepsilon \tag{5.23}$$

for all $x\in[-\pi, \pi]$.

Let us first suppose that the condition $f(-\pi)=f(\pi)$ is satisfied; we may then suppose $f(x)$ and $g_n(x)$ determined for all real x by their definition in the interval $[-\pi, \pi]$ and the conditions

$$f(x+2\pi)=f(x), \qquad g_n(x+2\pi)=g_n(x).$$

The periodic function $g_n(x)$ so defined can then be expressed as a Fourier series converging uniformly in every interval $[a, b]$. Hence, for sufficiently large m, we have

$$\left|g_n(x)-\left\{\tfrac{1}{2}A_0^{(n)}+\sum_{\mu=1}^{m}(A_\mu^{(n)}\cos\mu x+B_\mu^{(n)}\sin\mu x)\right\}\right|$$
$$=|g_n(x)-s_m^{(n)}(x)|<\tfrac{1}{2}\varepsilon, \tag{5.24}$$

where $A_\mu^{(n)}$ and $B_\mu^{(n)}$ are the Fourier coefficients of $g_n(x)$. It then follows from (5.23) and (5.24) that

$$|f(x)-s_m^{(n)}(x)|<\varepsilon, \tag{5.25}$$

from which we conclude that

$$\|f(x)-s_m^{(n)}(x)\|=\left\{\int_{-\pi}^{\pi}(f(x)-s_m^{(n)}(x))^2dx\right\}^{\frac{1}{2}}<\varepsilon\sqrt{(2\pi)}. \tag{5.26}$$

This shows that $f(x)$ can be approximated in mean with any desired accuracy by trigonometric sums. By the results of p. 56 the inequality in (5.26) will be satisfied *a fortiori* if $s_m^{(n)}(x)$ is replaced by

$$\tfrac{1}{2}a_0+\sum_{\mu=1}^{m}(a_\mu\cos\mu x+b_\mu\sin\mu x),$$

where a_μ and b_μ are the Fourier coefficients of $f(x)$.

If the relation $f(-\pi)=f(\pi)$ is not satisfied, or if the given function $f(x)$ is only sectionally continuous, we arrive at the same result by an obvious modification of the proof, which we leave to the reader.

Thus for all continuous functions $f(x)$ with Fourier coefficients a_ν and b_ν we have

$$\lim_{n\to\infty}\int_{-\pi}^{\pi}\left[f(x)-\left\{\tfrac{1}{2}a_0+\sum_{\nu=1}^{n}(a_\nu\cos\nu x+b_\nu\sin\nu x)\right\}\right]^2 dx$$

$$=\lim_{n\to\infty}\int_{-\pi}^{\pi}\{f(x)-\sigma_n(x)\}^2 dx$$

$$=\lim_{n\to\infty}\|f(x)-\sigma_n(x)\|^2=0. \tag{5.27}$$

This does *not* imply that in every case the equation

$$f(x)=\lim_{n\to\infty}\sigma_n(x)=\tfrac{1}{2}a_0+\sum_{\nu=1}^{\infty}(a_\nu\cos\nu x+b_\nu\sin\nu x) \tag{5.28}$$

holds for all values of x. Indeed we already know (§ 2.6) that continuous functions exist whose Fourier series do not converge at all points.

This result does not contradict the inequality (5.25); for there we were approximating the given function, for a certain value of ε, by means of a Fourier polynomial of a corresponding succession of line-segments. If we reduce the value of ε and at the same time pass to the succession of line-segments associated with a different sub-division of the interval, we arrive at a trigonometric polynomial having a different set of coefficients. This approximation cannot be improved by replacing the coefficients $A_\mu^{(n)}$, $B_\mu^{(n)}$ by the Fourier coefficients a_μ, b_μ of the function $f(x)$ itself. We proved (p. 56) that this was possible only for approximation in mean. For this reason we cannot draw from the inequality (5.25) the conclusion that the corresponding Fourier series represents the function.

§ **5.4. Schwarz's inequality.** From the rules (4.9) and (4.10) for the scalar product we can derive an important inequality. Let us take a linear combination of two (in general complex-valued) functions

$$u(x) = \bar{\lambda}f(x)+\mu g(x)$$

where μ is real, and

$$\lambda = \frac{(f,g)}{|(f,g)|}.$$

Then by (4.9) and (4.10)

$$0 \leqslant (u,u) = \mu^2(g,g)+\mu(g,f)\lambda+\bar{\lambda}(f,g)\mu+|\lambda|^2(f,f),$$

or, since $|\lambda| = 1$,

$$\mu^2(g,g)+\mu\left\{\frac{(g,f)(f,g)}{|(f,g)|}+\frac{(f,g)(g,f)}{|(f,g)|}\right\}+(f,f)\geqslant 0,$$

that is,

$$\mu^2(g,g)+2\mu\,|(f,g)|\,+(f,f)\geqslant 0. \tag{5.29}$$

The inequality (5.29) states that the parabola

$$y = ax^2+2bx+c, \tag{5.30}$$

with

$$a = (g,g),\ b = |(f,g)|,\ c = (f,f)$$

cannot cross the x-axis but can at most touch it (Fig. 12*a*,*b*,*c*). In the situation illustrated in Fig. 12*c*, real values of x would exist for which $ax^2+2bx+c<0$, which is impossible. Hence the quadratic function (5.30) cannot have two real distinct zeros. This means that $b^2 \leqslant ac$, i.e.

$$|(f,g)| \leqslant \|f\|\,\|g\|. \tag{5.31}$$

With our interpretation of the scalar product this may be written *in extenso* as

$$\left|\int_a^b f\bar{g}dx\right|^2 \leqslant \int_a^b |f|^2dx\int_a^b |g|^2dx. \tag{5.31'}$$

For vectors x and y in space of finite or infinite † dimension,

† See in this connection § 7.1.

that is, for

$$x = (x_1, x_2, \ldots, x_n), \qquad y = (y_1, y_2, \ldots, y_n)$$

or †

$$x = (x_1, x_2, \ldots, x_n, \ldots), \qquad y = (y_1, y_2, \ldots, y_n, \ldots)$$

we can derive, in an exactly similar way, the relation

$$|(x,y)| \leqslant \|x\| \, \|y\|, \tag{5.32}$$

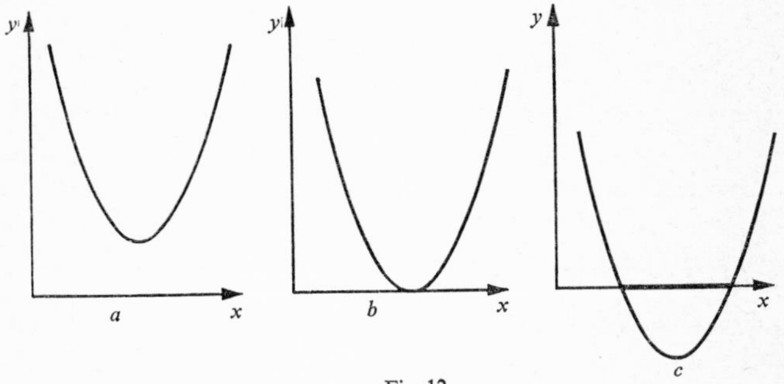

Fig. 12.

that is,

$$\left|\sum_{\nu=1}^{n} x_\nu \bar{y}_\nu\right|^2 \leqslant \sum_{\nu=1}^{n} |x_\nu|^2 \sum_{\nu=1}^{n} |y_\nu|^2 \tag{5.32'}$$

and

$$\left|\sum_{\nu=1}^{\infty} x_\nu \bar{y}_\nu\right|^2 \leqslant \sum_{\nu=1}^{\infty} |x_\nu|^2 \sum_{\nu=1}^{\infty} |y_\nu|^2. \tag{5.32''}$$

The inequality (5.31) (or (5.31′), (5.32), (5.32′) or (5.32″)) is known as **Schwarz's inequality.**

† In this case we impose the additional conditions $\sum_{\nu=1}^{\infty} |x_\nu|^2 < \infty$, $\sum_{\nu=1}^{\infty} |y_\nu|^2 < \infty$.

For continuous functions the sign of equality in (5.31) can hold only if $u(x) \equiv 0$. In this case $f(x)$ is a multiple of $g(x)$:

$$f(x) = -\frac{\mu}{\bar{\lambda}} g(x) = \nu g(x).$$

From (5.31) we readily obtain the so-called **triangle inequality** †:

$$\| f(x)+g(x) \| \leqslant \| f(x) \| + \| g(x) \|. \tag{5.33}$$

For we have

$$\| f(x)+g(x) \|^2 = (f+g,f)+(f+g,g)$$
$$\leqslant \| f+g \| (\| f \| + \| g \|),$$

from which (5.33) follows, provided $\| f+g \| \neq 0$. If we write $u(x)$ for $f(x)+g(x)$ and $v(x)$ for $g(x)$, we may write 5.33) in the alternative form

$$\| u(x) \| - \| v(x) \| \leqslant \| u(x)-v(x) \| . \tag{5.33'}$$

§ 5.5. The completeness of the Laguerre polynomials. Let C_1 be the class of functions $f(x)$ which are sectionally continuous for $0 \leqslant x < \infty$, and for which the integral

$$\int_0^\infty |f|^2 dx \tag{5.34}$$

exists. We shall show that for this class the Laguerre polynomials, defined by (4.60), are complete, the scalar product of two functions of the class C_1 being defined by (4.59).

† So named because the corresponding inequality for vectors x and y in space of two dimensions takes the form

$$\| x+y \| \leqslant \| x \| + \| y \| .$$

In geometric terms, this inequality states that the sum of two sides of a triangle is always greater than the third.

If we use Leibniz's rule for differentiation of a product,† according to which

$$\frac{d^n\{u(x)v(x)\}}{dx^n} = u^{(n)}(x)v(x)+\binom{n}{1}u^{(n-1)}(x)v'(x)+\ldots+$$
$$+\binom{n}{n-1}u'(x)v^{(n-1)}(x)+u(x)v^{(n)}(x),$$

we obtain from

$$\lambda_n(x) = e^x\,\frac{d^n(x^n e^{-x})}{dx^n}$$

the expansion

$$\lambda_n(x) = n!\sum_{k=0}^{n}(-1)^k\binom{n}{k}\frac{x^k}{k!}.$$

We now multiply by $(n!)^{-1}t^n$ and sum over n:

$$\sum_{n=0}^{\infty}\frac{\lambda_n(x)}{n!}t^n = \sum_{n=0}^{\infty}\sum_{k=0}^{n}(-1)^k\binom{n}{k}\frac{x^k t^n}{k!}.$$

Since $\binom{n}{k}$ vanishes for $k>n$, we may write the last expression in the form

$$\sum_{n=0}^{\infty}\frac{\lambda_n(x)}{n!}t^n = \sum_{k=0}^{\infty}\frac{(-1)^k x^k}{k!}\sum_{n=0}^{\infty}\binom{n}{k}t^n$$
$$= \sum_{k=0}^{\infty}\frac{(-1)^k x^k}{k!}\,\frac{t^k}{(1-t)^{k+1}} = \frac{e^{-xt/(1-t)}}{1-t}\,. \qquad (5.35)$$

By (4.56′) the functions

$$\lambda_n^*(x) = \frac{1}{n!}\lambda_n(x)$$

† The rule may readily be proved by induction.

are an orthonormal system for the interval $[0, \infty)$ with weighting function e^{-x}. An equivalent statement is that the functions

$$e^{-\frac{1}{2}x}\lambda_n^*(x) = l_n(x)$$

are an orthonormal system with weighting function 1. If we now multiply (5.35) by $e^{-\frac{1}{2}x}$, we obtain

$$g(x,t) = \frac{e^{-\frac{1}{2}(1+t)x/(1-t)}}{1-t} = \sum_{n=0}^{\infty} t^n l_n(x). \tag{5.36}$$

We now evaluate the integral

$$I_N(t) = \int_0^\infty \left\{ g(x,t) - \sum_{n=0}^{N} t^n l_n(x) \right\}^2 dx. \tag{5.37}$$

By (5.36) and the orthogonal property of the functions $l_n(x)$ we have:

$$(g,g) = \int_0^\infty g^2 dx = \sum_{n=0}^{\infty} t^{2n} = \frac{1}{1-t^2}, \qquad (g,l_n) = t^n.$$

By (5.37) this leads to

$$\| g(x,t) - \sum_{n=0}^{N} t^n l_n(x) \|^2 = \frac{1}{1-t^2} - \sum_{n=0}^{N} t^{2n},$$

or

$$\lim_{N\to\infty} I_N(t) = \lim_{N\to\infty} \| g(x,t) - \sum_{n=0}^{N} t^n l_n(x) \|^2 = 0. \tag{5.38}$$

We now put

$$t = \frac{\beta}{1+\beta}, \qquad 1-t = \frac{1}{1+\beta}, \tag{5.39}$$

and obtain from (5.37), in virtue of (5.36) and (4.56′):

$$I_N(t) = J_N(\beta)$$
$$= \int_0^\infty e^{-x} \left\{ e^{-\beta x}(1+\beta) - \sum_{n=0}^{N} \frac{\beta^n}{(1+\beta)^n} \frac{1}{n!} \lambda_n(x) \right\}^2 dx.$$

It then follows by (5.38) † that for arbitrary positive ε and sufficiently large $N = N(\beta)$, that

$$\left\| e^{-\beta x}(1+\beta) - \sum_{n=0}^{N} \left(\frac{\beta}{1+\beta}\right)^n \frac{\lambda_n(x)}{n!} \right\|_\lambda < \varepsilon,$$

or, if β is positive,

$$\left\| e^{-\beta x} - \frac{1}{1+\beta} \sum_{n=0}^{N} \left(\frac{\beta}{1+\beta}\right)^n \frac{\lambda_n(x)}{n!} \right\|_\lambda$$

$$= \left\| e^{-\beta x} - \sum_{n=0}^{N} b(\beta,n)\lambda_n(x) \right\|_\lambda < \frac{\varepsilon}{1+\beta} < \varepsilon. \qquad (5.40)$$

Now let $f(x)$ be a sectionally continuous function for $0 < x < \infty$, for which the integral (5.34) exists. We put $y = e^{-x}$, so that

$$f(x) = f(-\ln y) = h(y).$$

The function $h(y)$ is sectionally continuous in the interval $[0, 1]$. By Weierstrass's approximation theorem, this function can be approximated in mean by a polynomial. That is, for arbitrarily given $\eta > 0$ and sufficiently large m

$$\int_0^1 \left\{ h(y) - \sum_{\mu=0}^{m} a_\mu y^\mu \right\}^2 dy$$

$$= \int_0^\infty e^{-x} \left\{ f(x) - \sum_{\mu=0}^{m} a_\mu e^{-x\mu} \right\}^2 dx < \tfrac{1}{4}\eta^2. \qquad (5.41)$$

This may be written in the form:

$$\left\| f(x) - \sum_{\mu=0}^{m} a_\mu e^{-x\mu} \right\|_\lambda < \tfrac{1}{2}\eta. \qquad (5.42)$$

By (5.40) we also have

$$\left\| a_\mu e^{-x\mu} - \sum_{n=0}^{N(\mu)} a_\mu b(\mu,n)\lambda_n(x) \right\| < 2^{-\mu-2}\eta, \qquad (5.43)$$

provided we choose $\varepsilon < \eta |a_\mu|^{-1} 2^{-\mu-2}$.

† The norm $\| \quad \|_\lambda$ is the norm when the scalar product $(f,g)_\lambda$ is defined as in (4.59).

By (5.42), (5.43) and the triangle inequality, we now have

$$\left\|\left(f(x)-\sum_{\mu=0}^{m} a_\mu e^{-x\mu}\right)+\left(\sum_{\mu=0}^{m} a_\mu e^{-x\mu}-\sum_{\mu=0}^{m}\sum_{n=0}^{N(\mu)} a_\mu b(\mu,n)\lambda_n(x)\right)\right\|_\lambda$$

$$=\left\|f(x)-\sum_{\mu=0}^{m}\sum_{n=0}^{N[\mu]} a_\mu b(\mu,n)\lambda_n(x)\right\|_\lambda \leqslant \left\|f(x)-\sum_{\mu=0}^{m} a_\mu \mathrm{e}^{-x\mu}\right\| +$$

$$\sum_{\mu=0}^{m}\left\|a_\mu \mathrm{e}^{-x\mu}-\sum_{n=0}^{N[\mu]} a_\mu b(\mu,n)\lambda_n(x)\right\|_\lambda \leqslant \eta\left(\frac{1}{2}+\sum_{\mu=0}^{\infty}\frac{1}{2^{\mu+2}}\right)=\eta.$$

This shows that $f(x)$ can be approximated arbitrarily closely in mean by a series of Laguerre polynomials.

The completeness of the Hermite polynomials may be established in a similar way.

§ 5.6. Exercises

1. Using elementary methods, prove the special case of Schwarz's inequality:

$$\left(\sum_{\nu=1}^{2} a_\nu b_\nu\right)^2 \leqslant \sum_{\nu=1}^{2} a_\nu^2 \sum_{\nu=1}^{2} b_\nu^2.$$

2. Show that if $\sum_{\nu=1}^{n} x_\nu^2 = 1$, then $\left(\sum_{\nu=1}^{n} x_\nu\right)^2 \leqslant n.$

(An example of this is when $x_1 = \cos\alpha$, $x_2 = \sin\alpha$; in this case $(\cos\frac{1}{4}\pi+\sin\frac{1}{4}\pi)^2 = 2$.)

3. Prove $\int_a^b |f-\phi|^2 dx \leqslant 2\int_a^b |f-\psi|^2 dx + 2\int_a^b |\psi-\phi|^2 dx.$

4. Establish Weierstrass's approximation theorem in the form due to Bernstein, viz.—if $f(x)$ is continuous in the interval $[0, 1]$, then

$$\lim_{n\to\infty} B_n(x) = \lim_{n\to\infty} \sum_{k=0}^{n}\binom{n}{k} x^k(1-x)^{n-k} f\left(\frac{k}{n}\right) = f(x),$$

the equation holding uniformly in x.

CHAPTER VI

EIGENVALUE PROBLEMS IN MATHEMATICAL PHYSICS

§ **6.1. Schrödinger's equation.** One reason why the study of orthogonal systems of functions is so fruitful in practical mathematics is that many classes of functions may conveniently be represented by means of such systems. It turns out also that many boundary-value problems in the theory of differential and integral equations lead to orthogonal systems of functions. In such cases the class of solutions of the differential or integral equations may be represented by means of the system of orthogonal **eigenfunctions** associated with the problem. Thus representation by orthogonal systems arises naturally out of the formulation of the problem.

We begin with an example which plays an important part in modern atomic physics. The Schrödinger equation for the amplitude function † $u(x,y,z)$ of the 'electron wave' $\psi(x,y,z;t)$ is

$$-\frac{h^2}{8\pi^2 m}\nabla^2 u(x,y,z)+V(x,y,z)u(x,y,z) = Eu(x,y,z), \quad (6.1)$$

where E is the energy, h Planck's quantum of action, m the mass and $V = V(x,y,z)$ the potential energy of the system considered. It is useful to write equation (6.1) in the abbreviated form

$$\mathscr{H}u = Eu, \quad (6.2)$$

where $\mathscr{H}$ is the Hamiltonian operator

† The absolute value of the complex-valued function $u(x,y,z)$ is equal to the amplitude of the wave $\psi(x,y,z;t)$. See e.g. Born, *Atomic Physics*, p. 122.

$$\mathscr{H} = -\frac{h^2}{8\pi^2 m}\nabla^2 + V(x,y,z).$$

By the term 'operator' is meant in general a rule which associates with any element f of a class of functions an element g of the same or another class of functions. According to (6.2), the operator $\mathscr{H}$ applied to the unknown amplitude function $u(x,y,z)$ must reproduce this function $u(x,y,z)$ multiplied by E.

Let us first list some properties of the operator $\mathscr{H}$. Its linearity follows at once from its definition. For if a_1 and a_2 are any two complex numbers, it is clear that

$$\mathscr{H}(a_1 u_1 + a_2 u_2) = a_1 \mathscr{H} u_1 + a_2 \mathscr{H} u_2. \tag{6.3}$$

In order to formulate a further important property of the operator, we introduce a scalar product for the functions satisfying the operator equation (6.2). On physical grounds it is reasonable to consider only those solutions of (6.1) for which the integral

$$\int_{-\infty}^{\infty}\int_{-\infty}^{\infty}\int_{-\infty}^{\infty} |u(x,y,z)|^2 dxdydz$$
$$= \lim_{a\to\infty}\int_{-a}^{a}\int_{-a}^{a}\int_{-a}^{a} |u(x,y,z)|^2 dxdydz \tag{6.4}$$

exists.† For this to be so, it is necessary (but not sufficient) that the function should vanish at infinity. If the relation

$$\iiint_{-\infty}^{\infty} |u^2|\, dxdydz = 1 \tag{6.5}$$

is satisfied, the function is said to be normalised. The integral

$$(u,v) = \iiint_{-\infty}^{\infty} u(x,y,z)\overline{v(x,y,z)}dxdydz \tag{6.6}$$

† This condition is of the nature of a 'boundary condition' for the behaviour of the function at infinity.

is called the **scalar product** of the functions $u(x,y,z)$ and $v(x,y,z)$. By applying Schwarz's inequality to the integral

$$\iiint_{-a}^{a} u\bar{v}\,dx\,dy\,dz$$

we immediately see that the scalar product (6.6) always exists if the functions u and v are quadratically integrable, i.e. if the integrals (6.4) and

$$\iiint_{-\infty}^{\infty} |v|^2 dx\,dy\,dz \tag{6.4'}$$

exist. Now let u and v be two quadratically integrable functions on which the operator $\mathscr{H}$ can act. Then

$$(u,\mathscr{H}v) = (\mathscr{H}u,v). \tag{6.7}$$

To prove (6.7) we examine the difference

$$(\mathscr{H}u,v)-(u,\mathscr{H}v) = \iiint_{-\infty}^{\infty} (\mathscr{H}u\bar{v} - u\overline{\mathscr{H}v})\,dx\,dy\,dz. \tag{6.8}$$

We can write the integrand in (6.8) in the form

$$\mathscr{H}u\bar{v} - u\overline{\mathscr{H}v} = -\frac{h^2}{8\pi^2 m}(\bar{v}\nabla^2 u - u\overline{\nabla^2 v}) + (Vu\bar{v} - u\bar{V}\bar{v}). \tag{6.9}$$

Since the potential energy $V(x,y,z)$ is real, we have $V(x,y,z) = \overline{V(x,y,z)}$, so that the second bracket on the right of (6.9) vanishes. In the first bracket we now introduce the following transformations:

$$\bar{v}\frac{\partial^2 u}{\partial x^2} - u\frac{\partial^2 \bar{v}}{\partial u^2} = \frac{\partial}{\partial x}\left(\bar{v}\frac{\partial u}{\partial x} - u\frac{\partial \bar{v}}{\partial x}\right), \tag{6.10a}$$

$$\bar{v}\frac{\partial^2 u}{\partial y^2} - u\frac{\partial^2 \bar{v}}{\partial y^2} = \frac{\partial}{\partial y}\left(\bar{v}\frac{\partial u}{\partial y} - u\frac{\partial \bar{v}}{\partial y}\right), \tag{6.10b}$$

$$\bar{v}\frac{\partial^2 u}{\partial z^2} - u\frac{\partial^2 \bar{v}}{\partial z^2} = \frac{\partial}{\partial z}\left(\bar{v}\frac{\partial u}{\partial z} - u\frac{\partial \bar{v}}{\partial z}\right). \tag{6.10c}$$

On integrating with respect to x (6.10a) gives no contribution, since the quadratically integrable functions involved vanish at infinity, and similarly for (6.10b) and (6.10c), on integrating with respect to y and z respectively.

Hence the first bracket in (6.9) also vanishes; which proves (6.7).

In what follows we shall frequently be concerned with a class $\boldsymbol{K}$ of functions for which a scalar product is defined, obeying the usual rules of operation. An operator $\mathscr{T}$ defined in such a class $\boldsymbol{K}$ is said to be **Hermitian** † if it possesses the property

$$(u,\mathscr{T}v) = (\mathscr{T}u,v) \tag{6.11}$$

for all $u \in \boldsymbol{K}$, $v \in \boldsymbol{K}$. According to the foregoing results the Hamiltonian operator is linear and is Hermitian for the class of functions $u(x,y,z)$ for which the integral (6.4) exists.

Before dealing in greater detail with Schrödinger's equation (6.1), we now make some general observations about the properties of Hermitian operators.

§ 6.2. Eigenvalue problems for Hermitian operators.

Schrödinger's equation (6.1) or (6.2) is of the form

$$\mathscr{T}f = \mu f, \tag{6.12}$$

where $\mathscr{T}$ is a Hermitian operator, and μ a real or complex number. We look for solutions of equation (6.12) belonging to a certain class of functions. The non-zero values μ_ν of μ for which equation (6.12) is soluble are called the **eigenvalues** of the equation and the corresponding solutions $u_\nu(x)$ the **eigenfunctions.**

Not all Hermitian operators possess eigenvalues. This is shown by the simple example

$$\mathscr{T}f(x) = xf(x) \tag{6.13}$$

† After Charles Hermite (1822-1901).

for the class of functions continuous in the interval [0, 1]; the relation

$$xf(x) = \mu f(x)$$

is clearly impossible for $\mu \neq 0$. In many other cases such eigenvalues exist, together with the corresponding eigenfunctions. We shall not attempt to formulate sufficient conditions for the existence of eigenvalues. We shall confine ourselves meanwhile to summarising certain properties of eigenvalues and eigenfunctions.

If a Hermitian operator possesses eigenvalues, they are real.

For, since $(\mathscr{T}f,f) = \mu(f,f)$ it follows from $(\mathscr{T}f,f) = \overline{(\mathscr{T}f,f)} = (\mathscr{T}f,f)$ that $\mu = \bar{\mu}$, or in other words that μ is real.

The following result is of special importance:

The eigenfunctions belonging to different eigenvalues are orthogonal.

For let

$$\mathscr{T}u_i(x) = \mu_i u_i(x), \qquad \mathscr{T}u_k(x) = \mu_k u_k(x).$$

Then by (6.11) and the rules of operation for the scalar product,

$$\mu_i(u_i,u_k) = (\mathscr{T}u_i,u_k) = (u_i,\mathscr{T}u_k) = \bar{\mu}_k(u_i,u_k) = \mu_k(u_i,u_k),$$

so that

$$(\mu_i - \mu_k)(u_i,u_k) = 0.$$

Hence provided $\mu_i \neq \mu_k$, we do in fact have $(u_i,u_k) = 0$.

It may of course happen that there are several different eigenfunctions corresponding to a single eigenvalue. In such a case the eigenfunctions will not in general be orthogonal to each other. But if there are only a finite number of distinct linearly independent eigenfunctions belonging to a single eigenvalue, say the functions

$$v_i^{(1)}, v_i^{(2)}, \ldots, v_i^{(r)} \tag{6.14}$$

belonging to the eigenvalue μ_i, it is possible to orthogonalise the functions (6.14) by Schmidt's process and in this way to obtain a set $u_i^{(\rho)}$ ($\rho = 1,2,3,\ldots r$) of eigenfunctions which are orthogonal to each other and (by the previous results) to all the remaining eigenfunctions.

§6.3. Eigenvalues and eigenfunctions of the linear oscillator. We shall now investigate Schrödinger's equation (6.1) for the linear harmonic oscillator.† In this case n depends on a single variable x only, and the potential energy $V(x)$ is given by

$$V(x) = \tfrac{1}{2}m\omega_0^2 x^2.$$

Equation (6.1) then assumes the simple form

$$\frac{d^2u(x)}{dx^2} = \frac{8\pi^2 m}{h^2}\left(\frac{m\omega_0^2}{2}x^2 - E\right)u(x). \tag{6.15}$$

We try to solve this equation by putting

$$u(x) = v(x)e^{-m\omega_0\pi x^2/h} = v(x)e^{-\frac{1}{2}\alpha x^2}. \tag{6.16}$$

Then by (6.15) we obtain for the equation satisfied by $v(x)$

$$\frac{d^2v}{dx^2} - \frac{4m\omega_0\pi}{h}x\frac{dv}{dx} + \frac{8m\pi^2}{h^2}\left(E - \frac{h\omega_0}{4\pi}\right)v = 0. \tag{6.17}$$

Substitution of a power series

$$v(x) = \sum_{n=0}^{\infty} a_n x^n$$

for the unknown function in (6.17) then leads to the recurrence relation

$$a_{n+2} = a_n\left[\frac{4\pi m}{h^2}\left(\frac{h\omega_0(n+\frac{1}{2}) - 2\pi E}{(n+2)(n+1)}\right)\right]. \tag{6.18}$$

If we arbitrarily fix a_0 and a_1, we can calculate all the remaining coefficients of $v(x)$ by means of this recurrence

† This problem is treated in Schiff, *Quantum Mechanics*, Chapter IV.

relation. We are, however, interested only in those solutions of (6.15) for which the corresponding functions $u(x)$ (cf. (6.16)) are quadratically integrable.

Such solutions are to be expected only if the power series for $v(x)$ terminates at a certain term, in which case $v(x)$ is a polynomial. This may be seen as follows. From (6.18) we obtain for the coefficients a_n of $v(x)$ the limiting relation

$$\lim_{n\to\infty} \frac{a_{n+2}}{a_n}(n+2) = 2\alpha, \qquad \alpha = \frac{2\pi m\omega_0}{h}. \tag{6.19}$$

For the functions

$$h_1(x) = e^{\alpha x^2} = \sum_{n=0}^{\infty} b_n x^n = 1 + \alpha x^2 + \frac{\alpha^2}{2!}x^4 + \dots$$

and

$$h_2(x) = xe^{\alpha x^2} = \sum_{n=0}^{\infty} c_n x^n = x + \alpha x^3 + \frac{\alpha^2}{2!}x^5 + \dots$$

we also have

$$\lim_{n\to\infty} \frac{b_{n+2}}{b_n}(n+2) = \lim_{n\to\infty} \frac{c_{n+2}}{c_n}(n+2) = 2\alpha. \tag{6.20}$$

We may deduce from this that, if the series $v(x)$ does not terminate, it will exhibit the same asymptotic behaviour at infinity as a certain sum of the form

$$C_1 e^{\alpha x^2} + C_2 x e^{\alpha x^2}$$

with suitable coefficients C_1 and C_2. But this would imply that the function

$$u(x) = v(x)e^{-\frac{1}{2}\alpha x^2}$$

does not vanish at infinity, so that $u(x)$ would not be quadratically integrable; such solutions of the differential equation are of no interest to us.

So let us try to find polynomials satisfying equation (6.17). If a_{n+2} vanishes, we must have, for integral n,

$$E = E_n = (n+\tfrac{1}{2})\frac{h\omega_0}{2\pi}. \tag{6.21}$$

Physically this means that only discrete values of the energy of the oscillator, given by (6.21), occur. Whereas in Planck's theory the discrete energy levels given in advance were apt to appear as an arbitrary theoretical assumption, in Schrödinger's method the " quantisation " arises naturally out of the eigenvalue problem and boundary conditions, i.e. the behaviour of the functions at infinity.

To calculate the eigenfunctions, we put

$$\xi = x\sqrt{\left(\frac{2\pi m\omega_0}{h}\right)}. \tag{6.22}$$

We can then write the polynomials $v_n(x)$ in the form

$$v_n(x) = v_n^*(\xi) = b_0 + b_1\xi + b_2\xi^2 + \dots + b_n\xi^n,$$

and equation (6.18) gives, for the coefficients b_ν, the recurrence relation

$$b_{\nu+2} = b_\nu\frac{2(\nu-n)}{(\nu+2)(\nu+1)}. \tag{6.23}$$

The differential equation (6.17) is transformed by the substitution (6.22) into

$$\frac{d^2v_n^*}{d\xi^2} - 2\xi\frac{dv_n^*}{d\xi} + 2nv_n^*(\xi) = 0. \tag{6.24}$$

But this is the well-known differential equation (4.58) of the Hermite polynomials. We already know that for every n ($n = 0,1,2,3,\dots$) a well-defined polynomial of degree n exists. The polynomials belonging to different values of n are mutually orthogonal, with weighting function $e^{-\xi^2}$ (cf. (4.53)). The normalised solutions of the original equation (6.15) are, by (6.16) and (4.56), as follows:

$$u_n^*(\xi) = u_n(x) = (2^n n!)^{-\frac{1}{2}}\pi^{-\frac{1}{4}}H_n(\xi)e^{-\frac{1}{2}\xi^2}$$

i.e.

$$
\begin{aligned}
u_0^*(\xi) &= \pi^{-\frac{1}{4}} e^{-\frac{1}{2}\xi^2}, \\
u_1^*(\xi) &= \sqrt{2}\pi^{-\frac{1}{4}} \xi e^{-\frac{1}{2}\xi^2}, \\
u_2^*(\xi) &= \sqrt{2}\pi^{-\frac{1}{4}} (\xi^2 - \tfrac{1}{2}) e^{-\frac{1}{2}\xi^2}, \\
u_3^*(\xi) &= \sqrt{(\tfrac{4}{3})}\pi^{-\frac{1}{4}} (\xi^3 - \tfrac{3}{2}\xi) e^{-\frac{1}{2}\xi^2}, \\
&\dots\dots\dots\dots\dots\dots
\end{aligned}
\tag{6.25}
$$

§ 6.4. The stretched string subject to a transverse force. Suppose a string stretched at tension S between the points $x = 0$, $x = l$ and subject to a transverse force of magnitude P applied at the point $x = t$ (Fig. 13). We assume that P is much smaller than S, $P \ll S$, so that in equilibrium the inclinations α, β, to the x-axis of the two portions of the

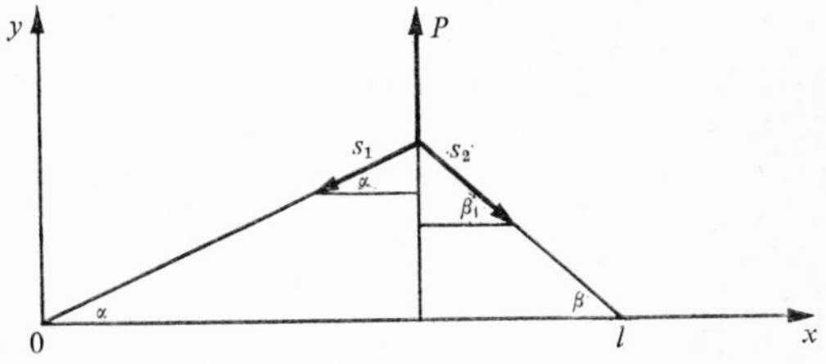

Fig. 13.

string are small, and their tensions s_1, s_2 are each approximately equal to S; thus $\sin\alpha \sim \tan\alpha$,† $\sin\beta \sim \tan\beta$, and $s_1 \sim s_2 \sim S$.

Resolving the forces acting on the point $x = t$ of the string along the y direction, we have as the condition for equilibrium, without approximation,

$$s_1 \sin\alpha + s_2 \sin\beta = P,$$

† The symbol $\sim$ denotes " is approximately equal to ".

or, making the approximation,

$$P \sim S\left(\frac{y}{t}+\frac{y}{l-t}\right) = S\frac{ly}{t(l-t)},$$

that is,

$$y(t) = \frac{P}{S}\frac{t(l-t)}{l}. \tag{6.26}$$

From this we may determine the displacements from equilibrium at points $x \leqslant t$ and $x \geqslant t$. We have (cf. Fig. 13)

$$\begin{aligned} (a)\quad x \leqslant t: &\qquad \frac{y(x)}{y(t)} = \frac{x}{t}, \\ (b)\quad x \geqslant t: &\qquad \frac{y(x)}{y(t)} = \frac{l-x}{l-t}. \end{aligned} \tag{6.27}$$

We now define a function $K(x,t)$ by

$$K(x,t) = \begin{cases} \dfrac{x(l-t)}{Sl} & \text{for} \quad x \leqslant t, \\ \dfrac{t(l-x)}{Sl} & \text{for} \quad x \geqslant t. \end{cases} \tag{6.28}$$

This function is obviously symmetric:

$$K(x,t) = K(t,x). \tag{6.29}$$

Using this function $K(x,t)$ we can by (6.27) (*a*) and (*b*) and (6.26) express the function $y(x)$ in the form

$$y(x) = PK(x,t). \tag{6.30}$$

If several forces P_ν ($\nu = 1,2,\ldots,n$) act at n different points t_ν, instead of one force P at a single point t, we have similarly

$$y(x) = \sum_{\nu=1}^{n} P_\nu K(x,t_\nu). \tag{6.30'}$$

If, finally, we pass to the case of a transverse force $w(t)dt$ distributed continuously along the string, we obtain by proceeding to the limit in (6.30′)

$$y(x) = \int_0^l w(t)K(x,t)dt. \tag{6.31}$$

Let us suppose that the function $y(x)$ is given by observation, but that the distribution of force $w(x)$ is unknown. Then (6.31) can be interpreted as an **integral equation** for the unknown function $w(x)$.

We shall return to the integral equation (6.31) later; but for the present we shall consider the problem from a slightly different viewpoint.

Suppose that the stretched string is rotating with angular velocity ω about the x-axis. Let its mass be uniformly distributed with unit line-density, so that we have $dm = dt$. The centrifugal force † $dm\omega^2 y = y\omega^2 dt$ now acts in place of the continuously distributed transverse force $w(t)dt$, and we therefore obtain from (6.31) for the equation governing the curve of deflection $y(x)$:

$$y(x) = \omega^2 \int_0^l y(t)K(x,t)dt. \tag{6.32}$$

In the integral equation ‡ (6.32) the unknown function $y(x)$ appears on the left side and under the integral sign in the form $y(t)$ as well. We can also write this equation as an operator equation

$$y(x) = \lambda \mathscr{T} y(x), \quad \lambda = \omega^2, \tag{6.32′}$$

where $\mathscr{T} y(x)$ is the integral operator

$$\mathscr{T} y(x) = f(x) = \int_0^l y(t)K(x,t)dt. \tag{6.33}$$

† See Rutherford, *Classical Mechanics*, p. 33.

‡ It is called a homogeneous integral equation *of the second kind*, while (6.31) is an equation *of the first kind* (for the unknown function $w(x)$).

Since all the functions involved are real, we have, by (6.29),

$$(\mathcal{T} y_1, y_2) = \int_0^l \int_0^l y_1(t) y_2(x) K(x,t) dx dt$$
$$= (y_1, \mathcal{T} y_2).$$

Hence the linear operator in (6.33) is Hermitian (cf. § 6.1), so that similar results hold for both the integral equation (6.32) and for the differential equation (6.1). By the results of § 6.2 the eigenfunctions $y_\nu(x)$ belonging to different eigenvalues λ_ν of the equation

$$y_\nu(x) = \lambda_\nu \mathcal{T} y_\nu(x)$$

are orthogonal, so that

$$(y_\nu, y_\mu) = \int_0^l y_\nu(x) y_\mu(x) dx = 0$$

for $\nu \neq \mu$.

In order to find these eigenfunctions and the corresponding eigenvalues, let us expand the function $K(x,t)$, which is called the **kernel** of the integral equation (6.32), in a Fourier series in the interval $(0, l)$.

For a fixed value of t, $K(x,t)$ is a sectionally linear function of x; it can therefore be expanded in the interval $(0, l)$ as a Fourier series of the form:

$$K(x,t) = \sum_{\nu=1}^{\infty} a_\nu(t) \sin \frac{\nu \pi x}{l}.$$

To see this, we suppose the function $K(x,t)$ defined in the interval $(-l, 0)$ (for the first variable) by $K(-x,t) = -K(x,t)$. We thereby define on *odd* functions in the interval $(-l, l)$, which can be expanded in a pure sine series. Since $K(0,t) = K(l,t) = 0$, this expansion converges in the *closed* interval $[0, l]$.

By the symmetry property (6.29), $a_\nu(t)$ must be of the form $b_\nu \sin \dfrac{\nu \pi t}{l}$, so that we have

$$K(x,t) = \sum_{\nu=1}^{\infty} b_\nu \sin \frac{\nu \pi x}{l} \sin \frac{\nu \pi t}{l}.$$

The coefficients b_ν can easily be determined by integration, the result being

$$K(x,t) = \frac{2l}{S\pi^2} \sum_{\nu=1}^{\infty} \frac{1}{\nu^2} \sin \frac{\nu \pi x}{l} \sin \frac{\nu \pi t}{l} = \sum_{\nu=1}^{\infty} \phi_\nu(x)\phi_\nu(t), \quad (6.34)$$

where

$$\phi_\nu(x) = \sqrt{\left(\frac{2l}{S}\right)} \frac{1}{\nu\pi} \sin \frac{\nu \pi x}{l},$$

and

$$(\phi_\nu, \phi_\mu) = \int_0^l \phi_\nu(x)\phi_\mu(x)dx = \frac{l^2}{\nu^2 \pi^2 S} \delta_{\nu\mu}. \quad (6.35)$$

Substituting (6.34) into (6.32), we obtain

$$y(x) = \omega^2 \sum_{\nu=1}^{\infty} \phi_\nu(x) \int_0^l \phi_\nu(t) y(t) dt. \quad (6.32'')$$

Now assume for $y(x)$ an expansion converging uniformly in x:

$$y(x) = \sum_{\mu=1}^{\infty} \alpha_\mu \phi_\mu(x).$$

Comparison of coefficients then gives, by (6.35),

$$\alpha_\nu = \omega^2 \sum_{\mu=1}^{\infty} \alpha_\mu \int_0^l \phi_\nu(t)\phi_\mu(t)dt = \frac{\omega^2 l^2}{\nu^2 \pi^2 S} \alpha_\nu, \quad (6.36)$$

so that

$$\omega^2 = \omega_\nu^2 = \frac{\nu^2 \pi^2 S}{l^2}. \quad (6.36')$$

Hence it is only for the eigenvalues

$$\lambda_\nu = \omega_\nu^2 = \frac{\nu^2 \pi^2 S}{l^2}$$

that the integral equation (6.32) or (6.32″) possesses non-zero solutions. If we now put $y(x) = \sum_{\nu=1}^{\infty} \alpha_\nu \phi_\nu(x)$ in (6.32′), with $\omega = \omega_\mu$, it follows, as above, that

$$\alpha_\nu = \omega_\mu^2 \alpha_\nu \frac{l^2}{\nu^2 \pi^2 S}$$

for given μ and all $\nu = 1, 2, 3, \ldots$. If α_ν did not vanish, we would have

$$\omega_\mu^2 = \frac{\nu^2 \pi^2 S}{l^2},$$

which according to (6.36′) is false for $\mu \neq \nu$. Hence for the eigenvalue ω_μ, $\alpha_\nu = 0$ for all values of ν which differ from μ. The eigenfunctions (normalised) belonging to the eigenvalues $\lambda_\nu = \omega_\nu^2$ are

$$y_\nu(x) = \frac{\nu\pi\sqrt{S}}{l} \sin \frac{\nu\pi x}{l}.$$

In the present instance the orthogonal functions used in the series expansion are just the eigenfunctions of our problem. We cannot expect to be equally fortunate in every case. However, even in more general cases representation by orthonormal systems often affords a useful means of solution. We can then try to achieve our object by solving systems of equations with an infinite number of unknowns. We must therefore interpolate a few remarks on the theory of such systems of equations.

§ 6.5. Systems of equations with an infinite number of unknowns. Let $\mathcal{T}$ be an integral operator † having a continuous kernel $K(x,t)$, so that

$$g(x) = \mathcal{T} f(x) = \int_a^b K(x,t) f(t) dt.$$

† These considerations also hold for other operators, under certain more general conditions.

It is required to find a function $y(x)$ continuous in the interval $[a, b]$, which satisfies the operator equation:

$$y(x) = \lambda \mathscr{T} y(x). \tag{6.37}$$

Let $\phi_\nu(x)$ be a complete orthonormal system for the class of functions continuous in $[a, b]$. We try to solve equation (6.37) by putting

$$y(x) = \sum_{\nu=1}^{\infty} x_\nu \phi_\nu(x), \tag{6.38}$$

with coefficients x_ν as yet unknown. Suppose such a solution exists, having a series expansion (6.38) converging uniformly in $[a, b]$. $\mathscr{T} y(x)$ is then also a continuous function; suppose it has the uniformly convergent expansion

$$\mathscr{T} y(x) = \sum_{\nu=1}^{\infty} b_\nu \phi_\nu(x) = \sum_{\nu=1}^{\infty} x_\nu \mathscr{T} \phi_\nu(x).$$

It follows from the orthogonality of the functions $\phi_\nu(x)$ that

$$b_\mu = \sum_{\nu=1}^{\infty} x_\nu (\mathscr{T} \phi_\nu, \phi_\mu). \tag{6.39}$$

If we now write for brevity

$$\alpha_{\nu\mu} = (\mathscr{T} \phi_\nu, \phi_\mu), \quad \nu = 1, 2, 3, \ldots, \quad \mu = 1, 2, 3, \ldots,$$

we have, by (6.37), for the unknown coefficients x_ν, the system of equations

$$\frac{x_\mu}{\lambda} = \sum_{\nu=1}^{\infty} x_\nu \alpha_{\nu\mu}, \qquad \mu = 1,2,3, \ldots,$$

or

$$\begin{aligned}
(\alpha_{11} - \lambda^{-1}) x_1 + \alpha_{21} x_2 + \alpha_{31} x_3 + \ldots &= 0, \\
\alpha_{12} x_1 + (\alpha_{22} - \lambda^{-1}) x_2 + \alpha_{32} x_3 + \ldots &= 0, \\
\ldots\ldots\ldots\ldots\ldots\ldots\ldots & \\
\alpha_{1n} x_1 + \alpha_{2n} x_2 + \ldots + (\alpha_{nn} - \lambda^{-1}) x_n + \ldots &= 0, \\
\ldots\ldots\ldots\ldots\ldots\ldots\ldots &
\end{aligned} \tag{6.40}$$

where the coefficients

$$\alpha_{\nu\mu} = \int_a^b \int_a^b K(x,t)\phi_\nu(t)\phi_\mu(x)dxdt$$

may be taken as known.

We know that the finite system of equations

$$\begin{aligned}(\alpha_{11}-\lambda^{-1})x_1+\ \ldots\ +\alpha_{n1}x_n &= 0,\\ \ldots\ldots\ldots\ldots\ldots\ldots\ldots &\\ \alpha_{1n}x_1+\ \ldots\ +(\alpha_{nn}-\lambda^{-1})x_n &= 0\end{aligned} \tag{6.40'}$$

is soluble only if the determinant $D_n(\lambda^{-1})$ of the coefficients of this set of equations vanishes. This gives n eigen values λ_ν^{-1} as the n roots of the equation $D_n(\lambda^{-1}) = 0$. Correspondingly, it can be shown that the system of equations (6.40) is soluble (if at all) only for a certain sequence of values λ_ρ ($\rho = 1,2,3,\ldots$). A theory of linear equations in an infinite number of unknowns exists † which yields a method for solving such systems of equations.

Provided the $\alpha_{\nu\mu}$ in (6.40) satisfy certain conditions, solutions $\{x_\nu^{(\rho)}\}$ do in fact exist for a sequence λ_ρ^{-1} of eigenvalues; and for these solutions the sum of the squares of the absolute values converges:

$$\sum_{\nu=1}^{\infty} |x_\nu^{(\rho)}|^2 < \infty. \tag{6.41}$$

We cannot develop this theory in greater detail here; the reader is referred to the book already mentioned. We may, however, remark that, at any rate for the integral operators considered here,‡ the existence of eigenvalues and of the corresponding eigenfunctions is assured. They can be determined, e.g. by using Schmidt's theory of linear equations.

† See e.g. Schmeidler, *Integralgleichungen*, Appendix.

‡ The existence of eigenvalues is in general assured for so-called completely continuous operators. See Meschkowski (2), or Schmeidler, *Linear Operators in Hilbert Space*.

The integral equation (6.31) can also be reduced to an infinite system of equations. Let us again suppose the given function $y(x)$ and the required function $w(x)$ to be represented by means of a suitable orthonormal system:

$$y(x) = \sum_{\nu=1}^{\infty} y_\nu \phi_\nu(x), \qquad w(x) = \sum_{\nu=1}^{\infty} w_\nu \phi_\nu(x).$$

If we now put

$$\int_0^l \int_0^l K(x,t)\phi_\mu(t)\phi_\nu(x)dxdt = \alpha_{\nu\mu}$$

and remember that

$$\int_0^l y(x)\phi_\nu(x)dx = y_\nu, \tag{6.42}$$

it follows from (6.31) by integration that

$$y_\nu = \sum_{\mu=1}^{\infty} \alpha_{\nu\mu} w_\mu, \qquad \nu = 1,2,3, \ldots, \tag{6.43}$$

or, more fully,

$$\begin{aligned} \alpha_{11}w_1 + \alpha_{12}w_2 + \alpha_{13}w_3 + \ldots &= y_1, \\ \alpha_{21}w_1 + \alpha_{22}w_2 + \alpha_{23}w_3 + \ldots &= y_2, \\ \ldots\ldots\ldots\ldots\ldots\ldots\ldots\ldots\ldots \end{aligned} \tag{6.44}$$

It is well-known that a finite system of equations

$$\sum_{\mu=1}^{n} \alpha_{\nu\mu} w_\mu = y_\nu \qquad (\nu = 1,2, \ldots, n)$$

can be solved by Cramer's rule, provided the determinant $\det\{\alpha_{\nu\mu}\} \neq 0$. Similarly it can be shown that under suitable conditions the system (6.44) admits precisely one solution

$$w_1, w_2, w_3, \ldots$$

for which $\Sigma|w_\nu|^2$ converges.† The relevant fact here is that the sum of the squares of the absolute values of the coefficients on the right of (6.44) also converges, $\Sigma|y_\nu|^2 < \infty$.

† For the solution of such systems of equations, see Chapter VIII.

This immediately follows from Bessel's inequality, since the coefficients y_ν are Fourier coefficients (cf. (6.42)).

§ 6.6. The converse problem. In solving the integral equations (6.31) and (6.32) we started with continuous functions which could be represented by means of orthonormal systems of continuous functions. The convergence of the sums of the squares of the corresponding Fourier coefficients followed from this.

Suppose now that we obtain by the method of linear equations a sequence of quantities y_ν (or w_ν), the sum of the squares of whose absolute values also converges. We can then interpret these quantities as the Fourier coefficients of the required functions $y(x)$ or $w(x)$.

The given functions, and also the kernel of the integral equation (the latter in respect of both variables) belonged to the class $C(a, b)$ of functions continuous in the interval $[a, b]$. The question now arises whether a function of class $C(a, b)$ exists for every sequence y_ν (or w_ν) such that $\Sigma|y_\nu|^2<\infty$ (or $\Sigma|w_\nu|^2<\infty$), which can be expressed as a uniformly convergent series

$$y(x) = \sum_{\nu=1}^{\infty} y_\nu\phi_\nu(x) \quad \text{or} \quad w(x) = \sum_{\nu=1}^{\infty} w_\nu\phi_\nu(x).$$

If this is not the case, a further question arises. Let $\phi_\nu(x)$ be a complete orthonormal system for the class $C(a, b)$, and let a_ν be an arbitrary sequence of complex numbers for which $\Sigma|a_\nu|^2$ converges. Is it possible to define a class $L(a, b)$ of functions to which the sums

$$\sum_{\nu=1}^{n} a_\nu\phi_\nu(x)$$

converge in mean? †

† Here we could of course consider ' ordinary ' convergence rather than mean convergence. But it turns out that the results can be expressed particularly simply if we take mean convergence as fundamental.

Both these questions are of great importance in applications. In practice, if we have to solve integral or other operator equations, we make use of approximations, which amount to determining the Fourier coefficients of the solution in some orthonormal system. It is therefore a matter of interest to anyone concerned with actually solving the equations to know whether it is possible in every case to find a continuous function as the solution of the problem.

It turns out that the classes $\boldsymbol{C}(a, b)$ and $\boldsymbol{L}(a, b)$ do not coincide. To be able to describe the class $\boldsymbol{L}(a, b)$, it is necessary to extend the concept of the Riemann integral, which we have used exclusively so far, in accordance with the ideas of Lebesgue. If all the integrals concerned, e.g. those for the Fourier coefficients, norms, etc., are understood in Lebesgue's sense, expansions in series of orthogonal functions can be obtained for certain functions which are not integrable in Riemann's sense. It is the extension of the concept in integration that makes it possible to define the class $\boldsymbol{L}(a, b)$.†

In this way functions exhibiting more or less complicated discontinuities are brought into the field of discussion. But this is inevitable. In the past, physicists have sometimes been inclined to dismiss as needless trifling the mathematicians' concern with such 'pathological' functions. It now appears that there are important practical problems which directly suggest the consideration of such functions.

§ 6.7. Exercises

1. It is shown in the theory of ordinary differential equations that the differential equation

$$y''(x)+Ay'(x)+\lambda y(x) = 0,$$

with the boundary conditions $y(a) = y(b) = 0$, is soluble only for a discrete series of eigenvalues $\lambda = \lambda_n$.

† See Chapter VII.

Show that the eigenfunctions belonging to different eigenvalues λ_n are orthogonal, the scalar product being defined as

$$(f,g) = \int_a^b fg dx.$$

2. If λ_n, $\phi_n(x)$ are the eigenvalues and eigenfunctions respectively of the integral equation

$$y(x) = \lambda \int_a^b K(x,t)y(t)dt, \qquad (6.45)$$

where the kernel $K(x,t)$ is continuous, prove that

$$\sum_{n=1}^{\infty} \frac{1}{\lambda_n^2} |\phi_n(x)|^2$$

converges for all $x \in [a, b]$.

3. If λ_n are the eigenvalues of (6.45), show that $\sum_{n=1}^{\infty} \lambda_n^{-2}$ converges.

4. Solve the inhomogeneous integral equation

$$y(x) = 1 + \int_0^1 xty(t)dt.$$

5. Show that the inhomogeneous integral equation associated with (6.45), namely

$$y(x) = \lambda \int_a^b K(x,t)y(t)dt + f(x) \qquad (6.46)$$

possesses the unique solution

$$y(x) = f(x) + \sum_{n=1}^{\infty} \frac{\lambda b_n}{\lambda_n - \lambda} \phi_n(x), \qquad b_n = \int_a^b f(t)\phi_n(t)dt,$$

provided λ differs from all the eigenvalues λ_n and $f(x)$ is not an eigenfunction of (6.45).

CHAPTER VII

HILBERT SPACES

§ 7.1. The sequence space $l^{(2)}$. The Fourier coefficients $a_\nu = (f,\phi_\nu)$ of the functions

$$f(x) \approx \sum_{\nu=1}^{\infty} a_\nu \phi_\nu(x)$$

which can be expanded in terms of the orthonormal system ϕ_ν have absolute values the sum of whose squares converges, by Bessel's inequality (4.8):

$$\sum_{\nu=1}^{\infty} |a_\nu|^2 < \infty. \tag{7.1}$$

It is appropriate to examine the properties of such sequences $\{a_\nu\}$ more closely. The set of sequences of complex numbers

$$a = \{a_1, a_2, a_3, \ldots\} \tag{7.2}$$

with the property (7.1) is known as the **Hilbert sequence space $l^{(2)}$**. The elements (7.2) of this space are called **vectors,** and the quantities a_ν the **components** of the vector a. It will appear that these vectors possess many properties familiar in connection with position vectors in n-dimensional space. For example:

The sum

$$x+y = \{x_1+y_1, x_2+y_2, x_3+y_3, \ldots\} \tag{7.3}$$

of two vectors with components x_ν and y_ν, $\nu = 1, 2, 3, \ldots$ is also a vector.

To prove this result, it is necessary to show merely that the sum $\Sigma\,|x_\nu+y_\nu|^2$ of the squares of the components of the sequence defined by (7.3) converges, i.e. that

$$\sum_{\nu=1}^{\infty} |x_\nu + y_\nu|^2 < \infty.$$

This is readily established. For

$$|x_\nu + y_\nu|^2 = (x_\nu + y_\nu)(\bar{x}_\nu + \bar{y}_\nu) = |x_\nu|^2 + |y_\nu|^2 + x_\nu \bar{y}_\nu + \bar{x}_\nu y_\nu.$$

$\Sigma\, |x_\nu|^2$ and $\Sigma\, |y_\nu|^2$ converge, by hypothesis; the convergence of $\Sigma x_\nu \bar{y}_\nu$ and $\Sigma \bar{x}_\nu y_\nu$ follows from the relation

$$|x_\nu \bar{y}_\nu| = |x_\nu|\, |y_\nu| \leqslant \tfrac{1}{2}(|x_\nu|^2 + |y_\nu|^2).$$

The sum

$$(x,y) = \sum_{\nu=1}^{\infty} x_\nu \bar{y}_\nu \tag{7.4}$$

is called the **scalar product** of x and y; the non-negative square root of

$$\| x \|^2 = (x,x) = \sum_{\nu=1}^{\infty} |x_\nu|^2$$

is known as the **norm** of the vector x. Clearly the norm vanishes if, and only if, x is the null-vector

$$\underline{0} = \{0,0,0, \dots\}.$$

The following rules of operation, analogous to those in (4.10), hold for the scalar product (x,y) defined by (7.4), α and β being any complex numbers:

$$\begin{aligned} (\alpha x, \beta y) &= \alpha \bar{\beta}(x,y), \\ (\alpha x + \beta y, z) &= \alpha(x,z) + \beta(y,z), \\ (x,y) &= \overline{(y,x)}. \end{aligned} \tag{7.5}$$

For the further development of the theory the concept of the **Cauchy sequence** † is of fundamental importance.

† The term *fundamental sequence* is also in common use in the literature.

A sequence $x^{(n)}$ $(n = 1,2,3, \ldots)$ *of vectors*

$$x^{(n)} = \{x_1^{(n)}, x_2^{(n)}, x_3^{(n)}, \ldots\}$$

is called a Cauchy sequence, if for every $\varepsilon > 0$ *there exists an integer* $N(\varepsilon)$ *such that*

$$\| x^{(n)} - x^{(m)} \| < \varepsilon \tag{7.6}$$

wherever $n > N(\varepsilon)$, $m > N(\varepsilon)$.

Furthermore, the vector x is said to be the limit of the sequence $x^{(n)}$ if for given arbitrary positive ε

$$\| x^{(n)} - x \| < \varepsilon \tag{7.7}$$

for sufficiently large n. We then write

$$x = \lim x^{(n)}. \tag{7.8}$$

According to (7.7), which is equivalent to

$$\sum_{\nu=1}^{\infty} | x_\nu^{(n)} - x_\nu |^2 < \varepsilon^2, \tag{7.7'}$$

we have, *a fortiori*, that $| x_\nu^{(n)} - x_\nu | < \varepsilon$ for sufficiently large n. That is, equation (7.7) implies that for each value of ν,

$$\lim_{n \to \infty} x_\nu^{(n)} = x_\nu \tag{7.9}$$

where the symbol ' lim ' is to be understood in the sense of ' ordinary ' analysis.

The converse of the above statement, however, is not true. If (7.9) holds for all integral ν, it does not follow that the limiting relation (7.8) holds.†

It is well known that for every Cauchy sequence $x^{(n)} = \{x_1^{(n)}, x_2^{(n)}, \ldots, x_m^{(n)}\}$ of vectors in m-dimensional space there is a vector x to which the sequence converges. *The corresponding result also holds for Cauchy sequences in the space* $\boldsymbol{l}^{(2)}$, as we shall now show.

By hypothesis we have, for $n > N(\varepsilon)$, $m > N(\varepsilon)$,

$$\| x^{(n)} - x^{(m)} \|^2 = \sum_{\nu=1}^{\infty} | x_\nu^{(n)} - x_\nu^{(m)} |^2 < \varepsilon^2, \tag{7.10}$$

† Cf. § 8.6, 1.

and therefore *a fortiori* $|x_\nu^{(n)}-x_\nu^{(m)}| < \varepsilon$ for all integral ν. It follows from Cauchy's well-known criterion for number-sequences that a sequence x_ν exists having the property (7.9).

These numbers x_ν define a vector

$$x = \{x_1,x_2,x_3,\ldots\}.$$

To justify the designation *vector*, we must show that $\Sigma|x_\nu|^2$ converges. For this purpose we use the 'triangle inequality', which also holds for our vectors,

$$\| a+b \| \leqslant \| a \| + \| b \|. \tag{7.11}$$

The relation (7.11) is proved by Schwarz's inequality in the same way as the corresponding equation (5.33) for functions. In particular, we have, for $a = x^{(m)}$, $b = x^{(n)}-x^{(m)}$,

$$\| x^{(n)} \| \leqslant \| x^{(m)} \| + \| x^{(n)}-x^{(m)} \|. \tag{7.11$'$}$$

By (7.10) it follows from (7.11′) that $\| x^{(n)} \|$ is uniformly bounded, since we have, for $n>N(\varepsilon)$ and any fixed $m>N(\varepsilon)$,

$$\| x^{(n)} \| \leqslant \| x^{(m)} \| + \varepsilon.$$

Hence a positive number k certainly exists for which

$$\sum_{\nu=1}^{M} |x_\nu^{(n)}|^2 < k \tag{7.12}$$

for all n, no matter how large M is chosen. By (7.9) it then follows from (7.12) that

$$\sum_{\nu=1}^{M} |x_\nu|^2 \leqslant k.$$

This shows that $\Sigma|x_\nu|^2$ converges, and hence that the sequence $\{x_1,x_2,x_3,\ldots\}$ represents a vector. We now show in a similar way that the sequence $x^{(n)}$ actually has the vector x as its limit. From the equation (cf. (7.10))

$$\sum_{\nu=1}^{M} |x_\nu^{(n)}-x_\nu^{(m)}|^2 \leqslant \varepsilon^2$$

for arbitrarily large M it follows that

$$\sum_{\nu=1}^{M} |x_\nu - x_\nu^{(m)}|^2 \leqslant \varepsilon^2$$

and hence also that

$$\sum_{\nu=1}^{\infty} |x_\nu - x_\nu^{(m)}|^2 \leqslant \varepsilon^2$$

for $m > N(\varepsilon)$.

§ **7.2. Definition of Hilbert space.** A set $\boldsymbol{R}$ of elements $x, y, z, \ldots$ called an **inner product space** if the following conditions are satisfied:

(a) An operation of **addition** (denoted by $+$) is defined in $\boldsymbol{R}$, for which $\boldsymbol{R}$ forms an Abelian group.†

(b) An operation of **multiplication** by complex numbers α, β, γ, ... is defined in $\boldsymbol{R}$, obeying the following rules:

$$\alpha(x+y) = \alpha x + \alpha y,$$
$$(\alpha+\beta)x = \alpha x + \beta x,$$
$$\alpha(\beta x) = (\alpha\beta)x,$$
$$1x = x,$$
$$0x = \underline{0}.$$

(c) With each pair of elements x, y of $\boldsymbol{R}$ there is associated a unique complex number (x,y), the **scalar product,** (or inner product) for which the rules (7.5) hold.

The non-negative square root $\| x \| = \sqrt{(x,x)}$ is called the **norm** of x. We now introduce a **metric** by defining the **distance** $\rho(x,y)$ between the elements x and y as $\| x-y \|$.

We are already familiar with a number of inner product spaces:

1. n-dimensional vector-space.
2. The sequence space $\boldsymbol{l}^{(2)}$,

† The null element of this group is denoted by $\underline{0}$.

3. The set $C(a, b)$ of functions continuous on the interval $[a, b]$. In this case the scalar product is given by

$$(f,g) = \int_a^b f(x)\overline{g(x)}dx.$$

Additional examples can readily be constructed using linear combinations

$$c_1\phi_1(x)+c_2\phi_2(x)+ \dots +c_n\phi_n(x)$$

of orthonormal functions associated with a scalar product

$$\int_a^b \rho(x)f(x)\overline{g(x)}dx$$

with any positive weighting function $\rho(x)$. For all inner product spaces Schwarz's inequality holds:

$$|(x,y)| \leqslant \| x \| \| y \| \tag{7.13}$$

as well as the triangle inequality

$$\| x+y \| \leqslant \| x \| + \| y \|. \tag{7.13'}$$

This is at once obvious from the fact that in the proof of the relations (5.31) and (5.33) only the characteristic properties of the scalar product for inner product spaces were used.

In modern functional analysis the concept of Hilbert space is of fundamental significance. In order to define it, we extend to arbitrary inner product spaces the notion, familiar in classical analysis, of the convergence of a sequence of vectors.

The definitions of convergence in the sequence space $\boldsymbol{l}^{(2)}$ given on p. 117 can be taken over word for word for arbitrary inner product spaces, and we then define the general Hilbert space as follows:

An inner product space $\boldsymbol{R}$ *is called a Hilbert space if every Cauchy sequence* $\{x^{(n)}\}$ *in it converges to an element* x *of the space in the sense of the metric* $\rho(x,y) = \|x-y\|$.

We now consider a few examples.

§ 7.3. Examples

(A) The n-dimensional euclidean space of the position vectors

$$x = \{x_1, x_2, x_3, \dots x_n\}$$

constitutes a Hilbert space, by well-known results of classical analysis.

(B) The sequence space $l^{(2)}$ of the vectors

$$x = \{x_1, x_2, x_3, \dots\}, \qquad \sum_{\nu=1}^{\infty} |x_\nu|^2 < \infty,$$

is a Hilbert space, according to the results of § 7.1.

(C) Let $\phi_\nu(x)$ $(\nu = 1,2,3, \dots)$ be an orthonormal system for the interval $[a, b]$ and the scalar product

$$(f,g) = \int_a^b f\bar{g}\,dx,$$

and let $\boldsymbol{L}$ be the set of linear combinations

$$a_1\phi_1(x) + a_2\phi_2(x) + \dots + a_n\phi_n(x) \tag{7.14}$$

of a *finite* number of elements of $\phi_\nu(x)$. This set clearly forms an inner product space which does not have the character of a Hilbert space. For let

$$f(x) = \sum_{\nu=1}^{\infty} a_\nu \phi_\nu(x), \qquad \sum_{\nu=1}^{\infty} |a_\nu|^2 < \infty,$$

and $a_\nu \neq 0$ for all ν. For simplicity we shall assume that this series converges uniformly in $[a, b]$. Then the sequence of partial sums

$$s_n(x) = \sum_{\nu=1}^{n} a_\nu \phi_\nu(x)$$

is certainly a Cauchy sequence of $\boldsymbol{L}$ which converges (also in norm) to $f(x)$, but not to an element of $\boldsymbol{L}$.

(D) According to § 4.2 the functions:

$$\Phi_\nu(z) = \left(\frac{\nu}{\pi}\right)^{\frac{1}{2}} z^{\nu-1} \qquad (\nu = 1,2,3, \ldots)$$

form an orthonormal system for the unit circle $|z| < 1$ in the complex plane. Let $\boldsymbol{R}_1$ be the set of functions which can be expressed in the unit circle in the form

$$f(z) = \sum_{\nu=1}^{\infty} a_\nu \Phi_\nu(z), \qquad \sum_{\nu=1}^{\infty} |a_\nu|^2 < \infty. \tag{7.15}$$

These functions (7.15) are power series

$$f(z) = \sum_{\nu=0}^{\infty} b_\nu z^\nu \tag{7.16}$$

where

$$b_\nu = a_{\nu+1}(\nu+1)^{\frac{1}{2}}\pi^{-\frac{1}{2}}, \qquad \nu = 0,1,2, \ldots \tag{7.16'}$$

The circle of convergence of this series has radius †

$$\rho = \left[\overline{\lim_{\nu\to\infty}} |b_\nu|^{1/\nu}\right]^{-1} = \left[\lim_{\nu\to\infty} \left| a_{\nu+1}\left(\frac{\nu+1}{\pi}\right)^{\frac{1}{2}} \right|^{1/\nu}\right]^{-1}.$$

Since $\Sigma|a_\nu|^2$ converges, ρ is certainly not less than 1. Hence the functions represented by (7.15) are analytic in the unit circle.

We can now set up a reversible one-one correspondence between the functions $f(z)$ of the space $\boldsymbol{R}_1$ having the series expansions (7.15) and the associated sequences

$$a = \{a_1, a_2, a_3, \ldots\}$$

of the sequence space $\boldsymbol{l}^{(2)}$. Elements corresponding to each other in this way have equal norms. For, using the rules for the scalar product, we can calculate

$$(f,f) = \iint |f|^2 dx dy$$

† Meschkowski (3) VII or Hyslop, *Infinite Series*, p. 79.

as follows:†

$$(f,f) = \left(\sum_{\nu=1}^{\infty} a_\nu \Phi_\nu(z), \sum_{\nu=1}^{\infty} a_\nu \Phi_\nu(z)\right) = \sum_{\nu=1}^{\infty} |a_\nu|^2 = (a,a).$$

Since every Cauchy sequence of $l^{(2)}$ converges to an element of $l^{(2)}$, the corresponding result also holds for the Cauchy sequences of $\boldsymbol{R}_1$. Hence $\boldsymbol{R}_1$ is a Hilbert space.

This space, however, is not identical with the set of all functions which are analytic in the unit circle. This set includes, for example, the power series

$$g(z) = \sum_{\nu=0}^{\infty} (\nu+1) z^\nu.$$

Its radius of convergence is $\rho = 1$; the Fourier coefficients are, by (7.16′), $a_{\nu+1} = \{\pi(\nu+1)\}^{\frac{1}{2}}$. Hence the series

$$\sum_{\nu=1}^{\infty} |a_\nu|^2 = \pi \sum_{\nu=0}^{\infty} (\nu+1)$$

diverges, and $g(z)$ does not belong to $\boldsymbol{R}_1$.

(E) The result obtained in (D) can readily be generalised to the set $\boldsymbol{R}(\boldsymbol{D})$ of functions which are regular, one-valued and quadratically integrable in a bounded domain $\boldsymbol{D}$ of finite connectivity in the complex plane; a function $f(z)$ is said to be **quadratically integrable** in $\boldsymbol{D}$ if the integral ‡

$$(f,f) = \iint_{D} |f(z)|^2 dx dy \tag{7.17}$$

† Schwarz's inequality gives $\lim (f_n, g) = (\lim f_n, g)$.

‡ Since the function $f(z)$ isnot necessarily bounded in $\boldsymbol{D}$, the integral (7.17) is defined by a limiting process. Let $\boldsymbol{D}_n$ be a sequence of closed sub-domains of $\boldsymbol{D}$ which exhaust $\boldsymbol{D}$, i.e. (*a*) $\boldsymbol{D}_n \subset \boldsymbol{D}_{n+k} \subset \boldsymbol{D}$: (b) every point of $\boldsymbol{D}$ belongs to a definite sub-domain $\boldsymbol{D}_m$ of the sequence. If the limit

$$\lim_{n\to\infty} \iint_{D_n} |f(z)|^2 dx dy$$

exists for all such sequences and has the same value J for all, the value of the integral (7.17) is defined as the value of J.

exists. To be able to call the set $\boldsymbol{R(D)}$ a Hilbert space, we must show that every Cauchy sequence $f_n(z)$ converges to an element of the set. Let $f_n(z)$ be such a sequence and let t be an arbitrary point of a closed † internal sub-domain $\boldsymbol{D'}$ of $\boldsymbol{D}$ (Fig. 14).

The function $f_m(z)-f_n(z)$ can then be expanded as a power series in a certain neighbourhood of t:

$$f_m(z)-f_n(z) = \sum_{\nu=0}^{\infty} c_\nu (z-t)^\nu. \tag{7.18}$$

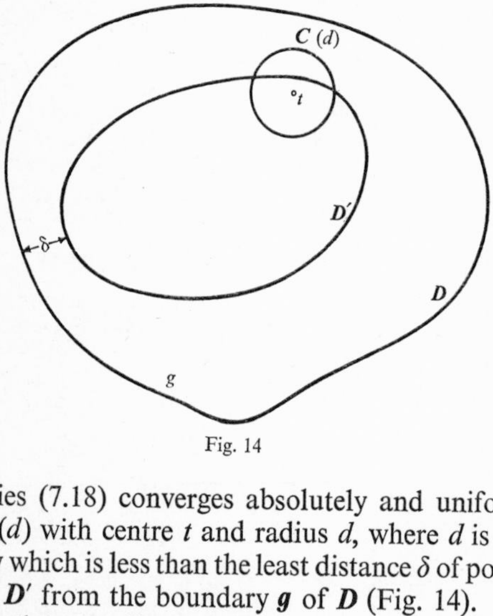

Fig. 14

The series (7.18) converges absolutely and uniformly in a circle $\boldsymbol{C}(d)$ with centre t and radius d, where d is a positive quantity which is less than the least distance δ of points of the domain $\boldsymbol{D'}$ from the boundary $\boldsymbol{g}$ of $\boldsymbol{D}$ (Fig. 14). By introducing polar coordinates

$$z-t = re^{i\phi}$$

we can easily evaluate the integral

$$I(\boldsymbol{C}) = \iint_{\boldsymbol{C}} |f_m(z)-f_n(z)|^2 dxdy = \iint_{\boldsymbol{C}} \left| \sum_{\nu=0}^{\infty} c_\nu r^\nu e^{i\nu\phi} \right|^2 r dr d\phi.$$

† A domain is said to be closed if it contains all its limit-points.

The result is

$$I(C) = \pi \sum_{\nu=0}^{\infty} \frac{|c_\nu|^2}{\nu+1} d^{2\nu+2},$$

whence it follows that

$$\| f_m(z) - f_n(z) \|^2 \geqslant I(C) \geqslant \pi |c_0|^2 d^2. \qquad (7.19)$$

But the coefficient c_0 of the power series expansion (7.18) is equal to $f_m(t) - f_n(t)$. Hence (7.19) gives

$$| f_m(z) - f_n(z) | \leqslant \| f_m(z) - f_n(z) \| / d\sqrt{\pi}. \qquad (7.20)$$

If now n and m are chosen so large ($n > N(\varepsilon), m > N(\varepsilon)$) that

$$\| f_m(z) - f_n(z) \| < \varepsilon, \qquad (7.21)$$

we have, by (7.20),

$$| f_m(t) - f_n(t) | < \varepsilon / d\sqrt{\pi}. \qquad (7.22)$$

It follows from (7.22) by Cauchy's criterion for sequences, that the limit

$$\lim_{n\to\infty} f_n(t) = f(t)$$

exists. Since it is possible to proceed to the limit uniformly in any closed sub-domain $\boldsymbol{D}'$ of $\boldsymbol{D}$, $f(t)$ is an analytic function throughout the interior of $\boldsymbol{D}$.

The function defined in this way is quadratically integrable; for, by the triangle inequality,

$$\| f_n \| \leqslant \| f_n - f_m \| + \| f_m \|.$$

Hence by (7.21),

$$| \| f_n \| - \| f_m \| | \leqslant \varepsilon$$

for $n > N(\varepsilon)$, $m > N(\varepsilon)$. This ensures that a limit

$$g = \lim_{n\to\infty} \| f_n \|$$

exists. The triangle inequality for the integrals over $\boldsymbol{D}'$ leads to

$$\left\{ \iint_{\boldsymbol{D}'} |f|^2 dxdy \right\}^{\frac{1}{2}} \leqslant \left\{ \iint_{\boldsymbol{D}'} |f - f_n|^2 dxdy \right\}^{\frac{1}{2}} + \left\{ \iint_{\boldsymbol{D}'} |f_n|^2 dxdy \right\}^{\frac{1}{2}}$$

for all closed sub-domains D' of D. This establishes the boundedness of the integral $\| f \|^2$.

The functions of the set $R(D)$ accordingly form a Hilbert space, in which the scalar product is given by †

$$(f,g) = \iint_D f(z)\overline{g(z)}dxdy \qquad (z = x+iy). \qquad (7.23)$$

(F) The question arises whether the set $C(a,b)$ of functions which are continuous on an interval $[a,b]$ of the real axis forms a Hilbert space. In Chapters II-V we were concerned in some detail with this class of functions, and in particular we proved that every function of $C(a,b)$ can be expressed in the form

$$f(x) \approx \tfrac{1}{2}a_0 + \sum_{\nu=1}^{\infty} (a_\nu \cos \nu x + b_\nu \sin \nu x).$$

More precisely, every function $f(x) \in C(a,b)$ can be approximated in mean arbitrarily closely by trigonometric polynomials

$$F_n(x) = \tfrac{1}{2}a_0 + \sum_{\nu=1}^{n} (a_\nu \cos \nu x + b_\nu \sin \nu x)$$

with

$$\sum_{\nu=1}^{\infty} (|a_\nu|^2 + |b_\nu|^2) < \infty.$$

We now ask the converse question: does every trigonometric series

$$\tfrac{1}{2}a_0 + \sum_{\nu=1}^{\infty} (a_\nu \cos \nu x + b_\nu \sin \nu x)$$

for which

$$\sum_{\nu=1}^{\infty} (|a_\nu|^2 + |b_\nu|^2) < \infty$$

† The existence of the integral (7.23) follows from Schwarz's inequality.

converge in mean to a continuous limiting function? The answer is that in general it does not. To obtain a Hilbert space it is necessary to supplement the set $C(a, b)$ by additional elements.

To enable us to define this more comprehensive set, it is necessary to introduce the concept of the **Lebesgue integral.** All the integrals considered so far were to be understood in the classical Riemannian sense. Following Lebesgue, we can modify the idea of an integral in such a way that a much wider class of functions becomes integrable than the class of functions integrable in Riemann's sense.

It then turns out that the set of functions which are quadratically integrable in Lebesgue's sense in an interval $[a, b]$ of the real axis forms a Hilbert space. To prove this, it is of course necessary to use the properties of this integral. As it is not possible, within the compass of a brief exposition of infinite series, to include the theory of the Lebesgue integral, we must confine ourselves to stating the facts and giving references to the literature.†

Let us accordingly assume that the set $L^2(a, b)$ of functions quadratically integrable in Lebesgue's sense in an interval $[a, b]$ of the real axis forms a Hilbert space, with the scalar product ‡

$$(f,g) = \int_a^b f\bar{g}\,dx.$$

§ 7.4. A criterion for the completeness of an orthonormal system. The definitions, given in Chapter IV, of linear independence and orthogonality of functions can immediately be transferred to the elements of arbitrary Hilbert

† The theory of the Lebesgue integral and its application to the theory of Hilbert spaces is described in Schmeidler (1), Riesz and Nagy, *Functional Analysis*, or Kolmogorov and Fomin, *Measure, The Lebesgue Integral and Hilbert Space.*

‡ The integral to be understood as a Lebesgue integral.

spaces. It follows that Schmidt's process of orthogonalisation, described in § 4.3, is applicable to the vectors of arbitrary Hilbert spaces, so that if a sequence of linearly independent vectors $x^{(n)}$ $(n = 1,2,3,\ldots)$ is given, it is always possible to obtain by linear combination

$$y^{(\nu)} = c_{\nu 1}x^{(1)} + c_{\nu 2}x^{(2)} + \ldots + c_{\nu\nu}x^{(\nu)}, \qquad \nu = 1,2,3,\ldots$$

a sequence of vectors $y^{(n)}$, for which †

$$(y^{(\nu)}, y^{(\mu)}) = \delta_{\nu\mu}, \qquad (\nu = 1,2,3,\ldots, \mu = 1,2,3,\ldots)$$

An orthonormal system $y^{(\nu)}$ in a Hilbert space $\boldsymbol{H}$ is said to be **complete** if every element $x \in \boldsymbol{H}$ can be expressed in the form ‡

$$x \approx \sum_{\nu=1}^{\infty} a_\nu y^{(\nu)} \approx \lim_{n\to\infty} \sum_{\nu=1}^{n} a_\nu y^{(\nu)}, \tag{7.24}$$

where the limit is to be taken in norm. In other words, (7.24) means that for every $\varepsilon > 0$ a number $N(\varepsilon)$ exists each such that

$$\left\| x - \sum_{\nu=1}^{n} a_\nu y^{(\nu)} \right\| < \varepsilon$$

provided $n > N(\varepsilon)$.

For example, according to these results, the system of functions

$$\left(\frac{\nu}{\pi}\right)^{\frac{1}{2}} z^{\nu-1} \qquad (\nu = 1,2,3,\ldots$$

† $\delta_{\nu\mu}$ is Kronecker's symbol:

$$\delta_{\nu\mu} = \begin{cases} 0 \text{ if } \nu \neq \mu, \\ 1 \text{ if } \nu = \mu. \end{cases}$$

‡ In the literature on Hilbert spaces expressions like (7.24) are usually written with the ordinary sign of equality. We adhere to the notation $\approx$ which helps to distinguish between pointwise convergence and convergence in norm—an important distinction for series of functions.

is a complete orthonormal system for the space $\boldsymbol{R}_1$ of functions which are regular and quadratically integrable in the unit circle of the complex plane.

The orthonormal system of the Fourier series considered in Chapter IV, viz.

$$\frac{1}{\sqrt{(2\pi)}}, \quad \frac{1}{\sqrt{\pi}} \cos \nu x, \quad \frac{1}{\sqrt{\pi}} \sin \nu x, \qquad (\nu = 1,2,3, \ldots)$$

is complete for the space $\boldsymbol{L}^2(-\pi, \pi)$ of functions which are quadratically integrable in Lebesgue's sense † in the interval $[-\pi, \pi]$. In Chapter IV we stated the completeness property only for the space $\boldsymbol{C}(-\pi, \pi)$ of functions *continuous* in the interval $[-\pi, \pi]$.

A corresponding statement holds for the Legendre polynomials in the interval $[-1, 1]$; the other orthonormal systems investigated in Chapter IV are also complete systems for certain Hilbert spaces.

A Hilbert space is said to be **separable** if it contains a complete sequence of orthonormal vectors. All the Hilbert spaces we have considered so far have been separable. But Hilbert spaces exist which do not possess this property. In such spaces we can of course orthogonalise each separate sequence of independent vectors, but none of the orthogonal sequences so obtained is complete. The situation is rather that in such non-separable spaces sets of mutually orthogonal elements exist, but these sets are non-denumerable.‡

We now give an important **criterion for completeness** of an orthogonal sequence.

The sequence $y^{(n)}$ $(n = 1,2,3, \ldots)$ *of orthonormal vectors in a Hilbert space* $\boldsymbol{H}$ *is complete if and only if the*

† See, e.g. Riesz and Nagy, *Functional Analysis*.
‡ Meschkowski (2), p. 21.

relation

$$(a, y^{(n)}) = 0$$

for all n implies $a = \underline{0}$.†

To prove this result we require Bessel's inequality

$$\sum_{n=1}^{\infty} |(x, y^{(n)})|^2 \leqslant (x, x), \tag{7.26}$$

which can be derived for general Hilbert spaces from the inequality

$$\left(x - \sum_{n=1}^{N} (x, y^{(n)}) y^{(n)},\ x - \sum_{n=1}^{N} (x, y^{(n)}) y^{(n)}\right) \geqslant 0$$

in the same way as in the special cases already considered (Chapter IV). In the general case of arbitrary Hilbert spaces the sign of equality again holds for complete systems $y^{(n)}$:

$$\sum_{n=1}^{\infty} |(x, y^{(n)})|^2 = (x, x). \tag{7.26'}$$

We preface the proof of the criterion with the remark that in Hilbert spaces we always have

$$\lim (x^{(n)}, y) = (\lim x^{(n)}, y) = (x, y) \tag{7.27}$$

for convergent vector sequences $x^{(n)}$ ($\lim x^{(n)} = x$). For by Schwarz's inequality we have

$$(x^{(n)} - x, y) \leqslant \| x^{(n)} - x \| \; \| y \|.$$

It immediately follows from (7.27) that the coefficients a_ν in the series representation (7.24) can be written as scalar products $a_\nu = (x, y^{(\nu)})$.

To establish the criterion, suppose first that the orthonormal system $y^{(\nu)}$ is complete in $\boldsymbol{H}$. Then every element

† Hamel, Schmeidler and others describe an orthonormal system having this property as *closed.* Glasman and others interchange the meanings of the terms *complete* and *closed.* Since, by the criterion to be proved, a sequence $y^{(n)}$ is closed if, and only if, it is complete (in whichever way these terms are chosen) this confusion in terminology can do no harm.

$x \in \boldsymbol{H}$ can be expressed in the form (7.28) with $a_\nu = (x, y^{(\nu)})$. If all these scalar products vanish, x is certainly the null vector.

Conversely, suppose we know that the relation $(x, y^{(\nu)}) = 0$ for all ν implies that x is the null vector, for a particular orthonormal system $y^{(\nu)}$ of the Hilbert space $\boldsymbol{H}$. Let a be an arbitrary vector of $\boldsymbol{H}$, and let a^* be the vector given by the sum

$$a^* \approx \sum_{\nu=1}^{\infty} (a, y^{(\nu)}) y^{(\nu)}.$$

By Bessel's inequality (7.26), $\sum |(a, y^{(\nu)})|^2 < \infty$, and hence a^*, being the limit of a Cauchy sequence, is a vector of our space $\boldsymbol{H}$. For the difference $a - a^*$ we then have

$$(a - a^*, y^{(\nu)}) = (a, y^{(\nu)}) - (a^*, y^{(\nu)}) = 0$$

for all ν. By hypothesis, $a - a^*$ then vanishes, and we have

$$a = a^* \approx \sum_{\nu=1}^{\infty} (a, y^{(\nu)}) y^{(\nu)}.$$

Every vector a can be expressed in this form; but this means that the system $y^{(\nu)}$ is complete.

The criterion just proved may be used to establish the completeness of classical orthonormal systems for certain Hilbert spaces.†

§ 7.5. Exercises

1. If $\phi_n(x)$ is the orthonormal system defined in Example (A) of § 4.2, prove that the set of functions which can be expressed in the form

$$f(x) = \sum_{\nu=1}^{\infty} a_\nu \phi_\nu(x), \qquad \sum_{\nu=1}^{\infty} |a_\nu|^2 < \infty,$$

forms a Hilbert function-space, all of whose functions are continuous.

† Kaczmarz and Steinhaus, *Theorie der Orthogonalreihen.*

2. Suppose the functions $\psi_n(x)$ ($n = 1,2,3,\ldots$) are defined in the interval $[-1, 1]$ by

$$\psi_n(x) = \begin{cases} 0 & -1 \leqslant x \leqslant 2^{-n-1}, \\ 2^{n+2}(x-2^{-n-1}) & 2^{-n-1} \leqslant x \leqslant 3 \cdot 2^{-n-2}, \\ -2^{n+2}(x-2^{-n}) & 3 \cdot 2^{-n-2} \leqslant x \leqslant 2^{-n}, \\ 0 & 2^{-n} \leqslant x \leqslant 1-2^{-n-1}, \\ 2^{n+3}\alpha_n(x-1+2^{-n-1}) & \\ & 1-2^{-n-1} \leqslant x \leqslant 1-3 \cdot 2^{-n-3} \\ -2^{n+3}\alpha_n(x-1+2^{-n-2}) & \\ & 1-3 \cdot 2^{-n-3} \leqslant x \leqslant 1-2^{-n-2}, \\ 0 & 1-2^{-n-2} \leqslant x \leqslant 1, \end{cases}$$

where the coefficients α_n are chosen so that for all n,

$$\int_{-1}^{1} \psi_n(x)^2 dx = 1.$$

Prove that the functions expressible in the form

$$f(x) = \sum_{n=1}^{\infty} a_n \psi_n(x), \qquad \sum_{n=1}^{\infty} |a_n|^2 < \infty,$$

from a Hilbert function-space, all of whose functions are continuous.

3. Show that the functions $e^{i\lambda x}$ form an orthonormal system for all real λ and the scalar product

$$(f,g) = \lim_{T\to\infty} \frac{1}{2T} \int_{-T}^{T} f(x)\overline{g(x)}dx.$$

CHAPTER VIII

THE SOLUTION OF LINEAR SYSTEMS

§ 8.1. Complete and incomplete systems in the space $l^{(2)}$. In Chapter VI it was shown that the boundary value problems of certain differential and integral equations lead to systems of equations in an infinite number of variables. We can now describe methods for solving systems of this kind, using theorems about Hilbert spaces, provided the coefficients satisfy certain conditions.

We write the general **inhomogeneous** system in the form

$$\sum_{k=1}^{\infty} a_{ik}x_k = b_i, \qquad i = 1,2,3,\ldots; \tag{8.1}$$

the corresponding **homogeneous** system is then

$$\sum_{k=1}^{\infty} a_{ik}x_k = 0, \qquad i = 1,2,3,\ldots. \tag{8.2}$$

We suppose the a_{ik} and b_i to be real; we also assume that the elements of each row of the matrix a_{ik}, and also the b_i, are components of vectors, so that

$$\sum_{k=1}^{\infty} a_{ik}^2 < \infty, \qquad i = 1,2,3,\ldots; \qquad \sum_{k=1}^{\infty} b_k^2 < \infty. \tag{8.3}$$

Such systems are particularly simple to deal with if the vectors

$$a^{(i)} = (a_{i1},a_{i2},a_{i3},\ldots) \tag{8.4}$$

form a complete orthonormal system. It is therefore important that the completeness of certain orthonormal systems in the space $l^{(2)}$ can be established by means of the following simple **criterion for completeness:**

A system of orthonormal vectors (8.4) *with real* a_{ik} *is complete if, and only if, the vectors formed from the columns of the matrix*

$$A = \begin{pmatrix} a_{11} & a_{12} & a_{13} \ldots \\ a_{21} & a_{22} & a_{23} \ldots \\ a_{31} & a_{32} & a_{33} \ldots \\ \ldots & \ldots & \ldots \\ \ldots & \ldots & \ldots \end{pmatrix} \tag{8.5}$$

that is, the vectors

$$A^{(k)} = (a_{1k}, a_{2k}, a_{3k}, \ldots) \tag{8.6}$$

form an orthonormal system.

For suppose first that the system (8.4) is complete for the Hilbert space $l^{(2)}$, so that we have

$$(a^{(i)}, a^{(j)}) = \sum_{k=1}^{\infty} a_{ik} a_{jk} = \delta_{ij}, \tag{8.7}$$

and by Bessel's equation (7.26′) we also have

$$(y,y) = \sum_{i=1}^{\infty} |(y, a^{(i)})|^2 \tag{8.8}$$

for every vector $y \in l^{(2)}$.

Now let $e^{(n)}$ be the vector

$$e^{(n)} = (0,0,0, \ldots 0,1,0,0, \ldots), \tag{8.9}$$

whose n-th component is equal to unity, while all the other components vanish; let $e^{(n,m)}$ be the vector

$$e^{(n,m)} = (0,0,0, \ldots, 0,1,0, \ldots, 0, 1, 0,0, \ldots),$$

which has unity as its n-th and m-th components and zero elsewhere. Then by (8.8)

$$1 = (e^{(n)}, e^{(n)}) = \sum_{i=1}^{\infty} (e^{(n)}, a^{(i)})^2 = \sum_{i=1}^{\infty} a_{in}^2 \tag{8.10}$$

and

$$2 = (e^{(n,m)}, e^{(n,m)}) = \sum_{i=1}^{\infty} (a_{im} + a_{in})^2. \tag{8.10'}$$

But it follows † from (8.10) and (8.10′) that

$$0 = 2-1-1 = \sum_{i=1}^{\infty} (a_{im}^2 + a_{in}^2 + 2a_{im}a_{in}) - \sum_{i=1}^{\infty} a_{im}^2 - \sum_{i=1}^{\infty} a_{in}^2,$$

or

$$\sum_{i=1}^{\infty} a_{im}a_{in} = 0. \tag{8.11}$$

By (8.10) and (8.11) the columns of the matrix (8.5) accordingly form an orthonormal system.

Conversely, let us assume that the columns of (8.5) form an orthonormal system:

$$(A^{(k)}, A^{(l)}) = \delta_{kl}. \tag{8.12}$$

Then it is possible to express the vectors $e^{(\nu)}$ defined by (8.9) in terms of the system of columns as follows:

$$e^{(\nu)} \approx a_{\nu 1}A^{(1)} + a_{\nu 2}A^{(2)} + a_{\nu 3}A^{(3)} + \ldots \tag{8.13}$$

This is immediately obvious if we substitute the several components of the vectors on both sides and take account of the orthogonality of the system $a^{(i)}$ of the rows.

We shall now draw the further inference that every vector $y \in l^{(2)}$ can be expressed by the system $A^{(k)}$ of the columns of (8.5). For this purpose we associate with the given vector y of components ‡ y_n another vector $y^{(n)}$, where

$$y^{(n)} = (y_1, y_2, y_3, \ldots, y_n, 0, 0, 0, \ldots)$$

having at most n non-zero components. Each of these vectors $y^{(n)}$, being a linear combination of a finite number only of vectors $e^{(\nu)}$,

$$y^{(n)} = \sum_{\nu=1}^{n} y_\nu e^{(\nu)}$$

† Note that the a_{ik} are assumed to be real.

‡ The y_n need not be real.

is then also expressible in terms of the system $A^{(\nu)}$:

$$y^{(n)} \approx (y^{(n)},A^{(1)})A^{(1)} + (y^{(n)},A^{(2)})A^{(2)} + \dots \qquad (8.14)$$

Furthermore,

$$\lim_{n\to\infty} \| y - y^{(n)} \| = 0, \qquad (8.15)$$

for, since y is a vector,

$$\lim_{n\to\infty} (|y_{n+1}|^2 + |y_{n+2}|^2 + \dots) = 0.$$

We now put

$$y \approx z + (y,A^{(1)})A^{(1)} + (y,A^{(2)})A^{(2)} + \dots \qquad (8.16)$$

and thus have, by (8.14) and (8.16),

$$\begin{aligned} y - y^{(n)} &\approx z + (y - y^{(n)},A^{(1)})A^{(1)} + (y - y^{(n)},A^{(2)})A^{(2)} + \dots \\ &\approx z + v^{(n)}. \end{aligned} \qquad (8.17)$$

Let us now calculate the norm of the vector $v^{(n)}$ defined by (8.17). We have, by (8.12),

$$(v^{(n)},v^{(n)}) = \sum_{\nu=1}^{\infty} |(y - y^{(n)},A^{(\nu)})|^2.$$

By Bessel's inequality (7.26), it then follows that

$$(v^{(n)},v^{(n)}) \leqslant (y - y^{(n)}, y - y^{(n)}),$$

or, by (8.15),

$$\lim_{n\to\infty} v^{(n)} = \underline{0}.$$

Hence by (8.15) and (8.17), z is the null vector, and by (8.16) every vector $y \in \boldsymbol{l}^{(2)}$ can be expressed in the form

$$y \approx \sum_{\nu=1}^{\infty} (y,A^{(\nu)})A^{(\nu)}.$$

The system $A^{(n)}$ is therefore complete.

If we are given an orthonormal system $x^{(n)}$ which is incomplete by our necessary and sufficient criterion, we can easily complement it so as to make it complete. To do this we express the vectors $e^{(n)}$ in terms of the system $x^{(n)}$; of course this is not possible without " remainders ". Suppose that

$$e^{(n)} \approx z^{(n)} + \sum_{\nu=1}^{\infty} (e^{(n)}, x^{(\nu)}) x^{(\nu)}. \tag{8.18}$$

The sequence of remainders $z^{(n)}$ is not necessarily linearly independent. To investigate the linear dependence we can use Gram's determinant (cf. § 4.3) and first obtain from the sequence $z^{(n)}$ of remainders a sequence $w^{(n)}$ of linearly independent vectors by omitting the linearly dependent elements. Orthogonalisation of this sequence $w^{(n)}$ by Schmidt's process † then yields a sequence $u^{(n)}$ of orthonormal functions. By (8.18) $(z^{(n)}, x^{(\nu)}) = 0$ for all n and ν. It follows that all the scalar products $(u^{(n)}, x^{(\nu)})$ also vanish for the vectors $u^{(n)}$ obtained by orthogonalisation.

The vectors

$$x^{(1)}, x^{(2)}, x^{(3)}, \ldots; \qquad u^{(1)}, u^{(2)}, u^{(3)}, \ldots \tag{8.19}$$

then form a complete orthonormal system. This can be seen as follows. By (8.18), the vectors $e^{(n)}$ can be expressed in the form

$$e^{(n)} \approx z^{(n)} + \sum_{\nu=1}^{\infty} (e^{(n)}, x^{(\nu)}) x^{(\nu)} = \sum_{\nu=1}^{N} \alpha_\nu u^{(\nu)} + \sum_{\nu=1}^{\infty} (e^{(n)}, x^{(\nu)}) x^{(\nu)},$$

since the $z^{(n)}$ are linear combinations of a finite number of elements $u^{(\nu)}$. It also follows, by the method used in proving our criterion, that an orthonormal system is certainly complete if its allows the vectors $e^{(n)}$ $(n = 1,2,3, \ldots)$ to be expressed in terms of it.

§ **8.2. Solution of the general homogeneous system.** The results of § 8.1 enable us to carry out the solution of the

† Schmidt's process of orthogonalisation (§ 4.3) can, as is readily seen, be applied in arbitrary Hilbert spaces.

systems of equations (8.1) and (8.2).† Let us first write the homogeneous system (8.2) in the form

$$(x,a^{(i)}) = 0, \quad i = 1, 2, 3, \ldots, \tag{8.20}$$

where x denotes the required vector $(x_1,x_2,x_3,\ldots)$, and $a^{(i)}$ the row vector $(a_{i1},a_{i2},a_{i3},\ldots)$. If we omit the linearly dependent vectors $a^{(i)}$, we arrive at a subsequence $A^{(j)}$, $(j = 1,2,3,\ldots)$ of the sequence $a^{(i)}$ and a corresponding system of equations

$$(x,A^{(j)}) = 0, \quad j = 1, 2, 3, \ldots. \tag{8.20'}$$

We can now orthogonalise the vector sequence $A^{(j)}$ by Schmidt's process and thus obtain the complete or incomplete system $v^{(k)}$ of orthogonal vectors

$$\begin{aligned} v^{(1)} &= c_{11}A^{(1)}, \\ v^{(2)} &= c_{21}A^{(1)}+c_{22}A^{(2)}, \\ &\ldots\ldots\ldots\ldots \\ v^{(k)} &= c_{k1}A^{(1)}+c_{k2}A^{(2)}+\ldots+c_{kk}A^{(k)}, \\ &\ldots\ldots\ldots\ldots \end{aligned} \tag{8.21}$$

With a view to later applications ‡ we note that we can of course solve this system of equations (8.21) for $A^{(1)}$, $A^{(2)}$, ... We obtain in this way an expression for the vectors $A^{(k)}$ in terms of the vectors $v^{(k)}$:

$$\begin{aligned} A^{(1)} &= \gamma_{11}v^{(1)}, \\ A^{(2)} &= \gamma_{21}v^{(1)}+\gamma_{22}v^{(2)}, \\ &\ldots\ldots\ldots\ldots \\ A^{(k)} &= \gamma_{k1}v^{(1)}+\gamma_{k2}v^{(2)}+\ldots+\gamma_{kk}v^{(k)}. \\ &\ldots\ldots\ldots\ldots \end{aligned} \tag{8.22}$$

† The following development—due to E. Schmidt—gives the general solution of the homogeneous and the inhomogeneous systems. The actual calculations are—if only because of the necessary investigation of linear dependence—not always entirely straightforward.

‡ The c_{ik}, γ_{ik} and the components of $A^{(k)}$ are all real, since the coefficients in (8.1) are real.

By (8.21) it now follows from (8.20′) that

$$(x,v^{(j)}) = 0, \quad j = 1, 2, 3, \ldots. \tag{8.20''}$$

Every solution of (8.20″) is also a solution of (8.20′) and *vice versa.*

If the orthonormal system $v^{(j)}$ is not complete, we can complement it by the method described in § 8.1 by adjoining a finite or denumerably infinite set of orthonormal vectors $d^{(j)}$. So let

$$v^{(1)},v^{(2)},v^{(3)},\ldots; \qquad d^{(1)},d^{(2)},d^{(3)},\ldots \tag{8.23}$$

be complete. The general solution of (8.20″) (or (8.20′) or (8.20)) can then be written in the form

$$x \approx \sum_{\nu=1}^{\infty} d_\nu d^{(\nu)}, \qquad \sum_{\nu=1}^{\infty} d_\nu^2 < \infty, \tag{8.24}$$

where the d_ν are the components of an arbitrary vector $d = (d_1,d_2,d_3,\ldots)$ in $l^{(2)}$. This can be seen as follows. Any vector $x \in l^{(2)}$ can be expressed in terms of the complete system (8.23) in the form

$$x \approx \sum_{\nu=1}^{\infty} (x,v^{(\nu)})v^{(\nu)} + \sum_{\nu=1}^{\infty} (x,d^{(\nu)})d^{(\nu)}. \tag{8.25}$$

If (8.20″) is satisfied, we obtain from (8.25) a representation of the type (8.24). Conversely, every vector (8.24) satisfies the system of equations (8.20″), since all the vectors $d^{(\nu)}$ are orthogonal to all the vectors $v^{(\nu)}$.

If the system $v^{(\nu)}$ is already complete, then according to (8.24) no solution of the given system of equations exists other than $\underline{0}$.

§ 8.3. Solution of the general inhomogeneous equation. To solve the general inhomogeneous system (8.1), we write the equations in the form

$$(x,a^{(i)}) = b_i, \quad i = 1, 2, 3, \ldots. \tag{8.26}$$

If there is a linear dependence between the vectors $a^{(i)}$ of the form

$$\alpha_1 a^{(1)} + \alpha_2 a^{(2)} + \ldots + \alpha_r a^{(r)} = \underline{0},$$

it is clear that (8.26) is soluble only if the b_i satisfy the corresponding relation

$$\alpha_1 b_1 + \alpha_2 b_2 + \ldots + \alpha_r b_r = 0.$$

If this necessary condition for the solubility of the system (8.26) is satisfied, we may omit the linearly dependent vectors from the sequence $a^{(i)}$ and replace the system (8.26) by

$$(x, A^{(k)}) = B_k, \quad k = 1, 2, 3, \ldots \tag{8.27}$$

where $A^{(k)}$ is the sequence of linearly independent vectors taken from the sequence $a^{(i)}$, and B_k is the corresponding sub-sequence of b_i. Every solution of (8.27) is then at the same time a solution of (8.26) and *vice versa*.

We now put (cf. (8.21))

$$\begin{aligned} C_1 &= c_{11} B_1, \\ C_2 &= c_{21} B_1 + c_{22} B_2, \\ &\cdots\cdots\cdots\cdots \\ C_k &= c_{k1} B_1 + c_{k2} B_2 + \ldots + c_{kk} B_k, \\ &\cdots\cdots\cdots\cdots \end{aligned} \tag{8.28}$$

and so obtain from (8.27), (8.28) and (8.21) the system of equations

$$(x, v^{(k)}) = C_k, \quad k = 1, 2, 3, \ldots \tag{8.29}$$

involving the orthonormal vectors $v^{(k)}$.

Let us suppose that the C_k are components of a vector, so that $\sum C_k^2 < \infty$. Then the vector

$$x \approx \sum_{k=1}^{\infty} C_k v^{(k)} \tag{8.30}$$

is a solution of the system (8.29). For we have

$$(x, v^{(k)}) = \left(\sum_{\lambda=1}^{\infty} C_\lambda v^{(\lambda)}, v^{(k)} \right) = C_k.$$

If the system $v^{(k)}$ is complete, the vector defined by (8.30) is clearly the only solution of the system (8.29). If on the other hand $v^{(k)}$ is not complete, and if the sequence

$$u^{(1)}, u^{(2)}, u^{(3)}, \ldots$$

completes the system $v^{(k)}$ to make a complete orthonormal system for the space $\boldsymbol{l}^{(2)}$, the general solution of (8.29) is

$$x \approx \sum_{k=1}^{\infty} C_k v^{(k)} + \sum_{k=1}^{\infty} \alpha_k u^{(k)}, \tag{8.31}$$

when the coefficients α_k have arbitrary complex values satisfying the condition $\sum |\alpha_k|^2 < \infty$. The solution (8.30) is in general the solution with the smallest norm; for

$$\sum_{k=1}^{\infty} C_k^2 + \sum_{k=1}^{\infty} |\alpha_k|^2 \geqslant \sum_{k=1}^{\infty} C_k^2.$$

§ 8.4. Explicit expression of the solution. It is useful, for practical calculations, to write down explicit approximate solutions of the systems (8.20) or (8.26).

To do this, we first express an arbitrary vector $y \in \boldsymbol{l}^{(2)}$ in terms of the complete system (8.23):

$$y \approx \sum_{i=1}^{\infty} (y, v^{(i)}) v^{(i)} + \sum_{k=1}^{\infty} (y, d^{(k)}) d^{(k)} \approx \sum_{i=1}^{\infty} (y, v^{(i)}) v^{(i)} + z,$$

where

$$z \approx \sum_{k=1}^{\infty} (y, d^{(k)}) d^{(k)} \approx y - \sum_{i=1}^{\infty} (y, v^{(i)}) v^{(i)}. \tag{8.32}$$

We now define

$$z^{(n)} \approx y - \sum_{i=1}^{n} (y, v^{(i)}) v^{(i)}. \tag{8.33}$$

By (8.24),

$$z = \lim_{n \to \infty} z^{(n)} \approx \sum_{k=1}^{\infty} (y, d^{(k)}) d^{(k)} \tag{8.34}$$

represents the general solution of (8.20″), an arbitrary vector of $l^{(2)}$ being taken for y.

The vector $z^{(n)}$ defined by (8.33) can alternatively be written as a determinant

$$z^{(n)} = \begin{vmatrix} (v^{(1)},v^{(1)}) & (v^{(1)},v^{(2)}) & \dots & (v^{(1)},v^{(n)}) & v^{(1)} \\ (v^{(2)},v^{(1)}) & (v^{(2)},v^{(2)}) & \dots & (v^{(2)},v^{(n)}) & v^{(2)} \\ \cdots & \cdots & \cdots & \cdots & \cdots \\ (v^{(n)},v^{(1)}) & (v^{(n)},v^{(2)}) & \dots & (v^{(n)},v^{(n)}) & v^{(n)} \\ (y,v^{(1)}) & (y,v^{(2)}) & \dots & (y,v^{(n)}) & y \end{vmatrix}. \tag{8.35}$$

For since $(v^{(i)},v^{(k)}) = \delta_{ik}$, we have, on expanding this determinant from the last column,

$$z^{(n)} = y-(y,v^{(1)})v^{(1)}-(y,v^{(2)})v^{(2)}- \dots -(y,v^{(n)})v^{(n)}.$$

We now define the determinants †

$$C_n = \begin{vmatrix} c_{11} & 0 & 0\dots 0 \\ c_{21} & c_{22} & 0\dots 0 \\ \cdots & \cdots & \cdots \\ c_{n1} & c_{n2} & \dots c_{nn} \end{vmatrix} = \begin{vmatrix} c_{11} & 0 & 0\dots 0 & 0 \\ c_{21} & c_{22} & 0\dots 0 & 0 \\ \cdots & \cdots & \cdots & \cdots \\ c_{n1} & c_{n2} & \dots c_{nn} & 0 \\ 0 & 0 & \dots 0 & 1 \end{vmatrix} \tag{8.36}$$

and

$$t^{(n)} = \begin{vmatrix} (A^{(1)},A^{(1)}) & \dots (A^{(1)},A^{(n)}) & A^{(1)} \\ (A^{(2)},A^{(1)}) & \dots (A^{(2)},A^{(n)}) & A^{(2)} \\ \cdots & \cdots & \cdots \\ (A^{(n)},A^{(1)}) & \dots (A^{(n)},A^{(n)}) & A^{(n)} \\ (y,A^{(1)}) & \dots (y,A^{(n)}) & y \end{vmatrix} \tag{8.37}$$

where $c_{\mu\nu}$ are the coefficients which enter in the orthogonalisation (8.21). By multiplying the rows of C_n into the columns of $t^{(n)}$ and remembering the rules of operation for

† C_n is a number, $t^{(n)}$ a vector.

scalar products, we obtain, using (8.21),

$$p^{(n)} = C_n t^{(n)} = \begin{vmatrix} (v^{(1)},A^{(1)}) \dots (v^{(1)},A^{(n)}) & v^{(1)} \\ \dots\dots\dots\dots\dots\dots & \dots \\ (v^{(n)},A^{(1)}) \dots (v^{(n)},A^{(n)}) & v^{(n)} \\ (y,A^{(1)}) \quad \dots (y,A^{(n)}) & y \end{vmatrix}. \tag{8.38}$$

We also have †

$$C_n p^{(n)} = C_n^2 t^{(n)} = z^{(n)}. \tag{8.39}$$

Now let

$$G_n = \begin{vmatrix} (A^{(1)},A^{(1)}) \dots (A^{(1)},A^{(n)}) \\ \dots\dots\dots\dots\dots\dots \\ (A^{(n)},A^{(1)}) \dots (A^{(n)},A^{(n)}) \end{vmatrix} \tag{8.40}$$

be the Gram's determinant of the linearly independent vectors $A^{(1)}$, $A^{(2)}, \dots A^{(n)}$. Then a similar calculation ‡ gives, by analogy with (8.39),

$$C_n^2 G_n = 1. \tag{8.41}$$

By (8.39) and (8.41) we now have an explicit expression for the vector $z^{(n)}$:

$$z^{(n)} = \begin{vmatrix} (A^{(1)},A^{(1)}) \dots (A^{(1)},A^{(n)}) & A^{(1)} \\ \dots\dots\dots\dots\dots\dots & \dots \\ (A^{(n)},A^{(1)}) \dots (A^{(n)},A^{(n)}) & A^{(n)} \\ (y,A^{(1)}) \quad \dots (y,A^{(n)}) & y \end{vmatrix} \div \det\{(A^{(i)},A^{(k)})\}. \tag{8.42}$$

By (8.34) or (8.24) the limit of this vector sequence represents the general solution of the given homogeneous system of equations (8.20).

It is possible to express the solution of least norm of the inhomogeneous system (8.1) or (8.26) in a similar way.

† By row-by-row multiplication.

‡ In this case we operate with the unbordered determinant C_n, cf. (8.36).

We write the vector (8.30) as the limit of a vector sequence $x^{(n)}$ in the form

$$x = \lim_{n\to\infty} x^{(n)} = \lim_{n\to\infty}\left(\sum_{k=1}^{n} C_k v^{(k)}\right),$$

and we then have for $x^{(n)}$

$$x^{(n)} = \begin{vmatrix} (v^{(1)},v^{(1)}) & \dots & (v^{(1)},v^{(n)}) & v^{(1)} \\ \dots & \dots & \dots & \dots \\ (v^{(n)},v^{(1)}) & \dots & (v^{(n)},v^{(n)}) & v^{(n)} \\ -C_1 & \dots & -C_n & 0 \end{vmatrix} \div \det\{(v^{(i)},v^{(k)})\}. \quad (8.43)$$

This is immediately obvious if we take account of the relations of orthogonality $(v^{(i)},v^{(k)}) = \delta_{ik}$.

We now note the determinant Γ_n of the system of equations (8.22):

$$\Gamma_n = \begin{vmatrix} \gamma_{11} & 0 & 0 & \dots 0 & 0 \\ \gamma_{21} & \gamma_{22} & 0 & \dots 0 & 0 \\ \dots & \dots & \dots & \dots & \dots \\ \gamma_{n1} & \gamma_{n2} & \gamma_{n3} & \dots \gamma_{nn} & 0 \\ 0 & 0 & 0 & \dots 0 & 1 \end{vmatrix} = \begin{vmatrix} \gamma_{11} & 0 & 0 \dots 0 \\ \gamma_{21} & \gamma_{22} & 0 \dots 0 \\ \dots & \dots & \dots \\ \gamma_{n1} & \gamma_{n2} & \dots \gamma_{nn} \end{vmatrix}. \quad (8.44)$$

If we now multiply the determinants forming the numerator and denominator of (8.43) by Γ_n^2 and take account of (8.22) and of the equations

$$\begin{aligned} B_1 &= \gamma_{11}C_1, \\ B_2 &= \gamma_{21}C_1 + \gamma_{22}C_2, \\ &\dots\dots\dots\dots \\ B_k &= \gamma_{k1}C_1 + \gamma_{k2}C_2 + \dots + \gamma_{kk}C_k, \\ &\dots \end{aligned} \quad (8.45)$$

which result from (8.28), we obtain for the vector $x^{(n)}$

$$x^{(n)} = \begin{vmatrix} (A^{(1)},A^{(1)}) & \dots & (A^{(1)},A^{(n)}) & A^{(1)} \\ \dots & \dots & \dots & \dots \\ (A^{(n)},A^{(1)}) & \dots & (A^{(n)},A^{(n)}) & A^{(n)} \\ -B_1 & \dots & -B_n & 0 \end{vmatrix} \div \det\{(A^{(i)},A^{(k)})\}. \quad (8.46)$$

Thus the approximate solution $x^{(n)}$ has been found in terms of the given vectors $A^{(k)}$ and the coefficients B_k.

§ 8.5. Mathieu's differential equation. Consider, as an example, Mathieu's differential equation

$$y''(x)+(\lambda+2\cos x)y(x) = 0. \tag{8.47}$$

The corresponding inhomogeneous equation is

$$y''(x)+(\lambda+2\cos x)y(x) = f(x), \tag{8.48}$$

where $f(x)$ is a given function. Let us confine ourselves to the case when $f(x)$ is an even function defined in the interval $[-\pi, \pi]$, whose associated Fourier series converges uniformly. We seek the even solutions of the equations (8.47) and (8.48) having a Fourier expansion

$$y(x) = \tfrac{1}{2}\alpha_0+\sum_{\nu=1}^{\infty}\alpha_\nu\cos\nu x. \tag{8.49}$$

We then have

$$y''(x) = -\sum_{\nu=1}^{\infty}\nu^2\alpha_\nu\cos\nu x \tag{8.49'}$$

and by substituting (8.49) and (8.49′) in the equation (8.47) we obtain

$$\sum_{\nu=1}^{\infty}(\lambda-\nu^2)\alpha_\nu\cos\nu x+\tfrac{1}{2}\lambda\alpha_0+\alpha_0\cos x+ 2\sum_{\nu=1}^{\infty}\alpha_\nu\cos\nu x\cos x = 0.$$

We now use the relation

$$2\cos\nu x\cos x = \cos(\nu+1)x+\cos(\nu-1)x$$

and collect the coefficients of $\cos\nu x$ ($\nu = 0,1,2,3,\ldots$):

$$(\tfrac{1}{2}\lambda\alpha_0+\alpha_1)+\sum_{\nu=1}^{\infty}\cos\nu x[(\lambda-\nu^2)\alpha_\nu+\alpha_{\nu-1}+\alpha_{\nu+1}] = 0. \tag{8.50}$$

The corresponding result for the inhomogeneous equation (8.48) is

$$(\tfrac{1}{2}\lambda\alpha_0+\alpha_1)+\sum_{\nu=1}^{\infty}\cos\nu x[(\lambda-\nu^2)\alpha_\nu+\alpha_{\nu-1}+\alpha_{\nu+1}]$$

$$=\tfrac{1}{2}c_0+\sum_{\nu=1}^{\infty}c_\nu\cos\nu x, \qquad (8.50')$$

where the c_ν are the Fourier coefficients of the given even function $f(x)$.

If in (8.50) we equate the several coefficients to zero, we arrive at the following system of equations:

$$\begin{aligned}\tfrac{1}{2}\lambda\alpha_0+\alpha_1 &= 0,\\ \alpha_0+(\lambda-1)\alpha_1+\alpha_2 &= 0,\\ \alpha_1+(\lambda-2^2)\alpha_2+\alpha_3 &= 0,\\ \dots\dots\dots\end{aligned} \qquad (8.51)$$

and so on for the unknown coefficients α_ν; in general

$$\alpha_{\nu-1}+(\lambda-\nu^2)\alpha_\nu+\alpha_{\nu+1}=0. \qquad (8.51')$$

In the same way we obtain from equation (8.50′) for the inhomogeneous equation:

$$\begin{aligned}\tfrac{1}{2}\lambda_0+\alpha_1 &= \tfrac{1}{2}c_0\\ \alpha_{\nu-1}+(\lambda-\nu^2)\alpha_\nu+\alpha_{\nu+1} &= c_\nu, \qquad \nu=1,2,3,\dots\end{aligned} \qquad (8.52)$$

We now put

$$\begin{aligned}&\alpha_\nu=x_{\nu+1}\ \text{for}\ \nu=0,1,2,3,\dots,\\ &a_{11}=\tfrac{1}{2}\lambda,\quad a_{12}=1,\\ &a_{\nu,\nu-1}=1,\quad a_{\nu\nu}=\lambda-\nu^2,\quad a_{\nu,\nu+1}=1\ \text{for}\ \nu=2,3,\dots,\\ &a_{\nu\mu}=0\ \text{for}\ \mu\neq\nu,\ \nu-1,\ \nu+1,\end{aligned} \qquad (8.53)$$

and thus obtain from (8.51) and (8.52) systems of equations of the form (8.20) or (8.26) treated in § 8.3. Here $\sum_k a_{ik}^2$ always converges; for in each row at most three coefficients differ from zero. We can easily form the scalar products of the row vectors

$$A^{(\nu)} = (0,0,0,\dots,0,1,\lambda-\nu^2,1,0,\dots)$$

which are clearly † linearly independent (if $\lambda \neq 2, \neq -1$). They are

$$(A^{(\nu)},A^{(\nu-1)}) = 2\lambda-2\nu^2+2\nu-1,$$
$$(A^{(\nu)},A^{(\nu+1)}) = 2\lambda-2\nu^2-2\nu-1,$$
$$(A^{(\nu)},A^{(\nu)}) = 2+\lambda^2-2\lambda\nu^2+\nu^4,$$

and

$$(A^{(\nu)},A^{(\mu)}) = 0$$

for

$$\mu \neq \nu, \ \neq \nu-1, \ \neq \nu+1, \text{ and } \nu = 2, 3, \dots$$

This determines the scalar products entering into the determinants of (8.42) and (8.46) and enables the approximate solutions $x^{(n)}$ to be calculated with any desired accuracy.

§ 8.6. Exercises

1. A vector sequence $s^{(n)}$ is defined in the space $l^{(2)}$ by:
$$s^{(n)} = ((n+1)^{-\frac{1}{2}}, (n+1)^{-\frac{1}{2}}, \dots (n+1)^{-\frac{1}{2}}, 2^{-1}(n+2)^{-\frac{1}{2}},$$
$$2^{-1}(n+2)^{-\frac{1}{2}} \dots, 3^{-1}(n+3)^{-\frac{1}{2}} \dots),$$
where each component $\{k(n+k)^{\frac{1}{2}}\}^{-1}$ occurs just $n+k$ times. Investigate the convergence of this sequence.
2. Prove the linear independence of the row vectors of the system of equations (8.51) for $\lambda \neq 2, \neq -1$.
3. Find an explicit expression in terms of determinants for the norm of the vector $z^{(n)}$ defined by (8.42).

† See § 8.6, 2.

CHAPTER IX

REPRODUCING KERNELS

§ 9.1. Definition of the kernel function. Let $\boldsymbol{H}$ be a separable Hilbert function-space with the complete orthonormal system $\phi_\nu(x)$, the functions $f(x)\in\boldsymbol{H}$ being defined over a certain point-set $\boldsymbol{E}$.† We now investigate the behaviour of the sum

$$K(x,t) = \sum_{\nu=1}^{\infty} \phi_\nu(x)\overline{\phi_\nu(t)}, \qquad x\in\boldsymbol{E}, \qquad t\in\boldsymbol{E}. \tag{9.1}$$

Let us suppose that this sum is uniformly convergent in x for fixed $t\in\boldsymbol{E}$ and that in addition (again for fixed $t\in\boldsymbol{E}$) $K(x,t)$ belongs to $\boldsymbol{H}$ as a function of x. Then the **kernel function** $K(x,t)$ defined by (9.1) and an arbitrary element $f(x)\in\boldsymbol{H}$ satisfy the equation ‡

$$(f(x),K(x,t))_x = (f(x),\sum_{\nu=1}^{\infty}\phi_\nu(x)\overline{\phi_\nu(t)})_x = \sum_{\nu=1}^{\infty}\phi_\nu(t)(f,\phi_\nu).$$

Since (f,ϕ_ν) $(\nu = 1,2,3,\ldots)$ are the Fourier coefficients of the function $f(x)$, and since the system $\phi_\nu(x)$ is complete, we have

$$f(t) = (f(x),K(x,t))_x. \tag{9.2}$$

Let us consider an example. By § 4.2 the system

$$\Phi_\nu(z) = \left(\frac{\nu}{\pi}\right)^{\frac{1}{2}} z^{\nu-1} \tag{9.3}$$

† $\boldsymbol{E}$ might for instance be an interval $[a, b]$ of the real axis, a domain $\boldsymbol{G}$ of the complex plane, or the curve $\mathbf{g}$ which is the boundary of such a domain.

‡ The suffix x indicates that the scalar product is to be taken with respect to x.

is a complete orthonormal system for the space $\boldsymbol{R}_1$ of analytic functions quadratically integrable in the unit disc **D** in the complex plane, and for the kernel function (9.1) we obtain

$$K(z,t) = \frac{1}{\pi} \sum_{\nu=1}^{\infty} \nu z^{\nu-1} \bar{t}^{\nu-1}.$$

But this is the binomial series for a known rational function; it converges absolutely for $|z| < 1$, $|t| < 1$. We thus have the expression

$$K(z,t) = \pi^{-1}(1 - z\bar{t})^{-2} \tag{9.4}$$

for the kernel function belonging to the system (9.3). In this case (9.2) yields the integral equation

$$f(t) = \iint_{\mathbf{D}} f(z)\overline{K(z,t)}\,dxdy = \frac{1}{\pi}\iint_{\mathbf{D}} \frac{f(z)dxdy}{(1-z\bar{t})^2}, \qquad z = x+iy. \tag{9.5}$$

In general, an operator of the type

$$\mathscr{T} f(t) = \iint f(z)\overline{A(z,t)}\,dxdy$$

associates with a given function $f(t)$ a different function $g(t)$:

$$\mathscr{T} f(t) = g(t).$$

The kernel function $K(x,t)$, however, possesses the **reproducing property** (9.5) (or (9.2) in the general case) that the image function $g(t)$ coincides with the original $f(t)$ for all functions $f(t)$ of the Hilbert function-space. We can write this in the form

$$\mathscr{K} f(t) = \iint_{\mathbf{D}} f(z)\overline{K(x,t)}\,dxdy = f(t).$$

Thus the operator $\mathscr{K}$ is the identity operator.

A fact of special significance is that the kernel function $K(x,t)$ is characteristic of the whole Hilbert space $\boldsymbol{H}$, and not of the particular complete system $\Phi_\nu(z)$ which has been chosen. The following important result holds:

A Hilbert function-space ***H*** *possesses at most one reproducing kernel.*

For suppose that a space $\boldsymbol{H}$ possesses two different reproducing kernels $K(x,t)$ and $K_1(x,t)$. These two functions $K(x,t)$ and $K_1(x,t)$ must then have the following properties:

(*a*) $f(t) = (f(x),K(x,t)) = (f(x),K_1(x,t))$ for all $f(x)\in\boldsymbol{H}$. (9.6)

(*b*) For all fixed $t\in\boldsymbol{E}$, $K(x,t)$ and $K_1(x,t)$ are elements of $\boldsymbol{H}$. It follows from this that

$$\begin{aligned} \| K(x,t)-K_1(x,t) \|_x^2 &= (K-K_1,K-K_1)_x \\ &= (K-K_1,K)_x-(K-K_1,K_1)_x \\ &= K(t,t)-K_1(t,t)-K(t,t)+K_1(t,t) \\ &= 0, \end{aligned} \tag{9.7}$$

since both kernel functions have been supposed to possess the reproducing property. Since according to (*b*) both are to be elements of $\boldsymbol{H}$, $K-K_1$ also belongs to $\boldsymbol{H}$, and (9.7) leads to $K-K_1 = \underline{0}$, that is, $K(x,t) = K_1(x,t)$.

This means that, if in a Hilbert function space $\boldsymbol{H}$ the sums

$$\sum_{\nu=1}^{\infty} \phi_\nu(x)\overline{\phi_\nu(t)}, \qquad \sum_{\nu=1}^{\infty} \psi_\nu(x)\,\overline{\psi_\nu(t)}$$

converge for two distinct complete orthonormal systems $\phi_\nu(x)$ and $\psi_\nu(x)$, then both sums are equal to the kernel function

$$K(x,t) = \sum_{\nu=1}^{\infty} \phi_\nu(x)\overline{\phi_\nu(t)} = \sum_{\nu=1}^{\infty} \psi_\nu(x)\overline{\psi_\nu(t)}. \tag{9.8}$$

The fact that the kernel function does not depend on the particular orthonormal system suggests dispensing with the orthonormal system in the definition and incorporating the reproducing property:

*Let **H** be a Hilbert function-space whose elements are functions over a certain set **E**. A function $K(x,t)$ $(x \in E, t \in E)$ is said to be the reproducing kernel of **H** (or alternatively the kernel function of **H**) if*

(a) *$K(x,t)$ belongs to **H** as a function of x, for all fixed $t \in E$,*

(b) *$K(x,t)$ possesses the reproducing property* (2).

This definition, given by Aronszajn,† makes it possible to introduce kernel functions for certain non-separable spaces as well. For separable spaces ‡ which are of particular importance in practice, the kernel function may always be expressed in the form (9.8) in terms of complete orthonormal systems.||

§ 9.2. Examples

Let us consider some further examples.

(A) The functions

$$\chi_\nu(z) = (2\pi)^{-\frac{1}{2}} z^{\nu-1}, \quad (\nu = 1,2,3, \ldots) \tag{9.9}$$

form an orthonormal system with respect to the scalar product

$$[f,g] = \int_{C_1} f\bar{g}\,ds \tag{9.10}$$

where C_1 denotes the circumference of the unit circle in the complex plane, and ds an element of its length. The functions expressible in terms of the system (9.9) in the form

$$f(z) = \sum_{\nu=1}^{\infty} a_\nu \chi_\nu(z), \qquad \sum_{\nu=1}^{\infty} |a_\nu|^2 < \infty, \tag{9.11}$$

† The development of the general theory of reproducing kernels on the basis of this definition can be found in Meschkowski (2).

‡ Cf. the definition on p. 129. || Cf. § 9.4, 3.

then form a Hilbert space $\boldsymbol{H}_s$.† It possesses a reproducing kernel

$$K_S(z,t) = \sum_{\nu=1}^{\infty} \chi_\nu(z)\overline{\chi_\nu(t)} = (2\pi)^{-1}(1-z\bar{t})^{-1}. \qquad (9.12)$$

(B) The orthonormal system defined by (4.13) is associated with the Hilbert space $\boldsymbol{H}_1$ of functions expressible in the form

$$f(x) = \sum_{\nu=1}^{\infty} a_\nu \phi_\nu(x), \qquad \sum_{\nu=1}^{\infty} |a_\nu|^2 < \infty.$$

This space also possesses a reproducing kernel. The convergence of the series for $K(x,t)$ readily follows from the fact that the terms of this series vanish from a certain term onwards, for all fixed x in the interval $[-1, 1]$.

(C) The Hilbert space $\boldsymbol{L}^2(a, b)$ of functions quadratically integrable in Lebesgue's sense in an interval $[a, b]$ does not possess a reproducing kernel. We confine ourselves to justifying this important observation for the interval $[-\pi, \pi]$. In this case the functions

$$\frac{1}{\sqrt{(2\pi)}}, \qquad \frac{1}{\sqrt{\pi}} \cos \nu x, \qquad \frac{1}{\sqrt{\pi}} \sin \nu x, \qquad \nu = 1,2,3,\ldots$$

form a complete orthonormal system. We see at once that the series (9.1) belonging to $x = t$, namely

$$\sum_{\nu=0}^{\infty} \{\phi_\nu(x)\}^2 = \frac{1}{2\pi} + \frac{1}{\pi} \sum_{\nu=1}^{\infty} (\cos^2 \nu x + \sin^2 \nu x)$$

diverges.

(D) It can easily be shown ‡ that the Hilbert space $\boldsymbol{H}_B(\boldsymbol{D})$ of functions which are one-valued, analytic and quadratically integrable in an arbitrary bounded domain $\boldsymbol{D}$

† The scalar product (9.10) and the associated orthonormal systems were first investigated by Szegö. Cf. Meschkowski (2), pp. 88 ff.

‡ Meschkowski (2), IV.

of finite connectivity in the complex plane possesses a reproducing kernel.†

The subset $H_B^*(D)$ ($H_B^*(D) \subset H_B(D)$) of functions having a unique integral in **D** forms a Hilbert space with a kernel.‡

We confine ourselves to giving the kernel function of the space $H_B^*(R)$ for the annulus $r < | z | < 1$. We start from the known fact that functions which are one-valued and analytic in the annulus *and possess a unique integral* can be expressed as a Laurent series in the form

$$f(z) = \sum_{\nu=-\infty}^{\infty}{}' a_\nu z^\nu. \tag{9.13}$$

The summation sign with an accent denotes that the term with $\nu = -1$ is absent; for we are concerned only with those functions whose integrals are unique; since the integral of z^{-1} does not possess this property in the annulus, the coefficient of z^{-1} in the expression for the functions of $H_B^*(R)$ must vanish.

Now the powers z^ν themselves form an orthogonal system (of course not yet normalised) for the annulus R and the scalar product

$$(f,g) = \iint_R f(z)\overline{g(z)}dxdy. \qquad (z = x + iy).$$

Normalisation yields the complete orthonormal system

$$\begin{aligned} \phi_\nu(z) &= \left\{\frac{\nu}{\pi(1-r^{2\nu})}\right\}^{\frac{1}{2}} z^{\nu-1}, \\ \phi_{-\nu}(z) &= \left\{\frac{\nu}{\pi(r^{-2\nu}-1)}\right\}^{\frac{1}{2}} z^{-\nu-1}, \qquad \nu = 1,2,3,\ldots \end{aligned} \tag{9.14}$$

† These kernel functions are known as *Bergman kernels*.

‡ In the case of simply connected domains these two spaces coincide, since by well-known results in the theory of functions every one-valued analytic function has a unique integral in a simply connected domain.

for the annulus $\boldsymbol{R}$ $(r<|z|<1)$. We obtain from this the kernel function †

$$K_{\mathrm{B}}^{*}(z,t)=(\pi z\bar{t})^{-1}\sum_{\nu=-\infty}^{\infty}{}' \frac{\nu z^{\nu}\bar{t}^{\nu}}{1-r^{2\nu}}. \tag{9.15}$$

If we use the series expression for the elliptic $\wp$-function, we may alternatively express the function $K_{B}^{*}(z,t)$ for the annulus in the explicit form

$$K_{\mathrm{B}}^{*}(z,t)=(\pi z\bar{t})^{-1}\{\wp(\ln z\bar{t}\,|\,2\pi i,2\ln r)+\alpha\},$$
$$\alpha=(\pi i)^{-1}\zeta(\pi i).$$

(E) The fact that the solution functions of certain elliptic differential equations in a domain $\boldsymbol{D}$ of the (x,y)-plane form a Hilbert space with kernel function is of importance in the theory of partial differential equations. This is true for harmonic functions, but it also holds for the solutions of the equation

$$\frac{\partial^2 u}{\partial x^2}+\frac{\partial^2 u}{\partial y^2}=\nabla^2 u=c(x,y)u(x,y), \qquad c(x,y)>0. \tag{9.16}$$

In this case the scalar product of two solutions is given by

$$(u,v)=\iint_{\boldsymbol{D}}(u_x v_x+u_y v_y+cuv)\,dx\,dy. \tag{9.17}$$

It now turns out ‡ that the set of solution functions of (9.16) for which the integral

$$(u,u)=\|u\|^2=\iint_{\boldsymbol{D}}(u_x^2+u_y^2+cu^2)\,dx\,dy$$

exists form a Hilbert space with a kernel function. This kernel function may be used to solve certain boundary-value problems of the equation (9.16). The knowledge of this

† The accented summation sign in (9.15) denotes that $\nu=0$ is omitted.

‡ Meschkowski (2), Chapter XI.

kernel function is therefore of great importance for the practical solution of the associated partial differential equation.†

The kernel functions of the spaces $\boldsymbol{H_B(D)}$ and $\boldsymbol{H_B^*(D)}$, on the other hand, are important in connection with the theory of conformal mapping. The mapping functions for normal regions can readily be found explicitly by means of reproducing kernels.‡

§ 9.3. Properties of spaces with a kernel function. In the representation of elements of the space $\boldsymbol{L}^2$ it was necessary to distinguish (cf. § 5.1) between mean convergence (denoted by $\approx$) and pointwise convergence (denoted by $=$). Continuous functions exist whose associated Fourier series do not converge pointwise, but converge in mean.

In the case of Hilbert function-spaces possessing a reproducing kernel, however, the situation is essentially simpler. The following result holds:

In a Hilbert function-space possessing a kernel, convergence in norm implies pointwise convergence.

To prove this we start from a sequence $f_n(x)\in \boldsymbol{H}$ which converges in norm to an element $f(x)\in \boldsymbol{H}$. Suppose that

$$\| f_n(x)-f(x) \| <\varepsilon \tag{9.18}$$

for $n>N(\varepsilon)$. Then by (9.2) we have, for $x\in \boldsymbol{E}$,

$$f_n(t)-f(t) = (f_n(x)-f(x),\ K(x,t)).$$

From this it follows, by Schwarz's inequality (7.13) that

$$| f_n(t)-f(t) | \leqslant \| f_n(x)-f(x) \| \ \| K(x,t) \|_x. \tag{9.19}$$

But again by the reproducing property (9.2) of the kernel function,

$$\| K(x,t) \|_x^2 = (K(x,t),\ K(x,t))_x = K(t,t). \tag{9.20}$$

† Cf. Bergman and Schiffer, *Kernel functions and Elliptic Differential Equations.*

‡ Meschkowski (2), Chapter VII.

Hence (9.18) and (9.19) lead to

$$|f_n(t)-f(t)| \leqslant \varepsilon\{K(t,t)\}^{\frac{1}{2}}. \tag{9.21}$$

But this means that the sequence $f_n(t)$ converges to $f(t)$ for any fixed $t \in \boldsymbol{E}$, that is,

$$f(t) = \lim_{n\to\infty} f_n(t),$$

in the sense of pointwise convergence.

An immediate consequence is that we may pass from the series representation of the elements of any function-space possessing a kernel,

$$f(x) \approx \sum_{n=1}^{\infty} a_n \phi_n(x) \tag{9.22}$$

to their representation by a convergent series in the sense of pointwise convergence,

$$f(x) = \sum_{n=1}^{\infty} a_n \phi_n(x). \tag{9.22'}$$

For by (9.22), if ε is arbitrarily given and m and n sufficiently large,

$$\left\| \sum_{\nu=m}^{\infty} a_\nu \phi_\nu(x) \right\| < \varepsilon,$$

from which it follows by the above method of proof that

$$\left| \sum_{\nu=m}^{n} a_\nu \phi_\nu(x) \right| < \varepsilon\{K(x,x)\}^{\frac{1}{2}}.$$

We may add that the convergence $f_n(x) \to f(x)$ is uniform in any sub-domain $\boldsymbol{E}'$ of $\boldsymbol{E}$ in which $K(x,x)$ is uniformly bounded.

We conclude this chapter with an extremal theorem from the general theory of spaces possessing a kernel, which admits of many applications.

The absolute value of any function $f(x) \in \boldsymbol{H}$ of unit norm is at most equal to the absolute value of $K(x,t)\{\| K(x,t) \|_x\}^{-1}$ at the point $x = t$, $t \in \boldsymbol{E}$.

Conversely,

The function $K(x,t)\{K(t,t)\}^{-1}$ has the smallest norm of all the functions $f(x)$ of a Hilbert function-space possessing a kernel function $K(x,t)$, which take the value 1 at the point $x = t$.

Each of these extremal statements can readily be deduced from (9.20). We first write (9.20) in the form

$$\{K(t,t)\}^{\frac{1}{2}} = \frac{K(t,t)}{\| K(x,t) \|_x}. \tag{9.20'}$$

By Schwarz's inequality we deduce from (9.2) that

$$| f(t) | \leqslant \| f(x) \| \; \| K(x,t) \|_x = \| f(x) \| \{K(t,t)\}^{\frac{1}{2}}, \tag{9.23}$$

and from (9.20′) and (9.23) we obtain the inequality

$$\frac{| f(t) |}{\| f(x) \|} \leqslant \frac{K(t,t)}{\| K(x,t) \|_x} \tag{9.24}$$

or

$$\frac{\| K(x,t) \|_x}{K(t,t)} \leqslant \frac{\| f(x) \|}{| f(t) |}. \tag{9.24'}$$

This proves both extremal theorems.

Thus for example in the space $\boldsymbol{R}_1$ with the kernel function (9.4) we have the following results:

(*a*) *An upper bound can be given for the modulus of all functions analytic and quadratically integrable in the unit disc* $\boldsymbol{D}$ *which satisfy the condition*

$$\iint_{\boldsymbol{D}} | f |^2 \, dxdy = 1,$$

viz.

$$| f(t) |^2 \leqslant \pi^{-1}(1 - | t |^2)^{-2}.$$

(b) For all functions which are analytic and quadratically integrable in the unit disc **D** *and which take the value 1 at the point* $t(|t|<1)$ *we have*

$$\iint_D |f(x)|^2 dxdy \geqslant \pi^{-1}(1-|t|^2)^{-2}.$$

§ 9.4. Exercises

1. Show that the kernel-function $K(x,t)$ of the Hilbert space defined in § 7.4, 2 possesses the following properties:
   (a) $K(x,t)$ is continuous for all fixed values of t.
   (b) The function $k(x) = K(x,x)$ is discontinuous at $x = 0$.
2. Show that every sub-space $\boldsymbol{H}'$ of a Hilbert function-space $\boldsymbol{H}$ possessing a kernel also possesses a reproducing kernel.
3. Prove that the kernel function of a Hilbert function-space $\boldsymbol{H}$ defined by the reproducing property is expressible by an orthonormal system $\phi_\nu(x)$ in the form

$$K(x,t) = \sum_{\nu=1}^{\infty} \phi_\nu(x)\overline{\phi_\nu(t)}$$

   if, and only if, $\boldsymbol{H}$ is separable.
4. Given a Hilbert space $\boldsymbol{H}$ possessing a kernel, determine a function of $f \in \boldsymbol{H}$ with the least possible norm, for which

$$f(a_n) = b_n, \ (n = 1,2,3, \dots, N),$$

   where $a_n \in \boldsymbol{E}$, and the b_n are arbitrary complex constants.

SOLUTIONS OF THE EXERCISES

Chapter I. INTERPOLATING SERIES

1. Start from the identity

$$\frac{1}{z} = \frac{1}{z+\alpha} + \frac{\alpha}{z+\alpha} \cdot \frac{1}{z}$$

and substitute $h, h+1, h+2, \ldots$ in succession for α.

2. (a) Converges for all $z \neq 0, -1, -2, \ldots$.
(b) Converges for all z.
(c) Converges for $|z| < 1$, diverges for $|z| > 1$.

3. Verify by substitution.

4. The substitution $x = 1-e^{-t}$ leads to

$$I(z) = \int_0^1 x^{-1}\{1-(1-x)^{z-1}\}dx.$$

Application of the binomial theorem then gives

$$I(z) = \sum_{\mu=1}^{\infty} \frac{(-1)^{\mu-1}}{\mu}\binom{z-1}{\mu}.$$

Chapter II. TRIGONOMETRIC SERIES

1. $2\sum_{n=1}^{\infty}(-1)^{n-1}\frac{\sin nx}{n}$.

2. $\frac{1}{\pi}+\frac{1}{2}\sin x-\frac{2}{\pi}\sum_{n=1}^{\infty}\frac{\cos 2nx}{4n^2-1}$.

3. $\frac{\pi^2}{3}+4\sum_{n=1}^{\infty}\frac{(-1)^n \cos nx}{n^2}$.

4. $\sum_{n=1}^{\infty}\left(\frac{2\pi^2}{n}-\frac{12}{n^3}\right)\sin x.$

5. $-\frac{1}{2}\sin x+2\sum_{n=2}^{\infty}\frac{(-1)^n n}{n^2-1}\sin nx.$

6. $\sum_{n=1}^{\infty}\frac{\cos nx}{n^2}.$

7. $-\sum_{n=1}^{\infty}\frac{\cos nx}{n}.$

8. $\frac{4\pi^2}{3}+4\sum_{n=1}^{\infty}\frac{\cos nx}{n^2}-4\pi\sum_{n=1}^{\infty}\frac{\sin nx}{n}.$

CHAPTER III. EXAMPLES AND APPLICATIONS

1.(a) $-\frac{4}{\pi}\sum_{n=2}^{\infty}\frac{n\cos\frac{1}{2}n\pi}{n^2-1}\sin n\pi x.$

(b) $\frac{1}{2}\sin\pi x-\frac{4}{\pi}\sum_{n=1}^{\infty}\frac{(-1)^n n}{4n^2-1}\sin 2n\pi x.$

(c) $\frac{1}{4}-\frac{2}{\pi^2}\sum_{n=1}^{\infty}\frac{\cos 2(2n-1)\pi x}{(2n-1)^2}$

2. Put $x = 0$ and $x = \pi$ and obtain

$$\frac{\pi^2}{12}=1-\frac{1}{2^2}+\frac{1}{3^2}-\frac{1}{4^2}+\ldots;$$

$$\frac{\pi^2}{6}=1+\frac{1}{2^2}+\frac{1}{3^2}+\frac{1}{4^2}+\ldots.$$

3. Substitute $x = 0$ in (3.8).

4. $\cosh x=\frac{2}{\pi}\sinh\pi\left[\frac{1}{2}+\sum_{n=1}^{\infty}(-1)^n\frac{\cos nx}{1+n^2}\right],$

$\sinh x=\frac{2}{\pi}\sinh\pi\sum_{n=1}^{\infty}(-1)^{n-1}\frac{n}{1+n^2}\sin nx.$

5. For $x = \frac{1}{2}\pi$ we obtain

$$\frac{\pi^3}{8} = 2\pi^2\{1-\frac{1}{3}+\frac{1}{5}- \ldots\}-12\left\{1-\frac{1}{3^3}+\frac{1}{5^3}-\frac{1}{7^3}+ \ldots\right\}.$$

The series in the first bracket is equal to $\frac{1}{4}\pi$ (Hyslop, *Infinite Series*, p. 81). Hence

$$\frac{\pi^3}{32} = 1-\frac{1}{3^3}+\frac{1}{5^3}-\frac{1}{7^3}+\ldots.$$

6. $f(x) = x^2$ has step-discontinuities of amount $4\pi^2$ at the points $0, 2\pi, 4\pi, \ldots$. Hence the series represents the value $\frac{1}{2}(4\pi^2+0) = 2\pi^2$ at these points. By the solution of Exercise II, 8 above, we obtain, for $x = 0$,

$$2\pi^2 = \frac{4\pi^2}{3}+4\sum_{n=1}^{\infty}\frac{1}{n^2}.$$

7.(a) $\frac{1}{2}x \cos x+\frac{1}{4} \sin x$.

(b) $$\frac{4-2 \cos x}{5-4 \cos x}.$$

Chapter IV. ORTHONORMAL SYSTEMS

1. $$\int_0^\pi \cos nx \cos mx dx = 0, \qquad n \neq m,$$

$$\int_0^\pi \cos^2 nx dx = \tfrac{1}{2}\pi.$$

2. $$\int_0^{\frac{1}{2}\pi} \sin (2n-1)x \sin (2m-1)x dx = 0, \qquad n \neq m,$$

$$\int_0^{\frac{1}{2}\pi} \sin^2 (2n-1)x dx = \tfrac{1}{4}\pi.$$

3. The function $\phi_\nu(x)$ ($\phi_3(x)$ is shown in Fig. 15) is constant in each of 2^ν intervals $J_N(N = 1,2,3, \ldots, 2^\nu)$. By the

definition of the functions $\phi_\nu(x)$ we have, for $\mu > \nu$,

$$\int_{J_N} \phi_\nu(x)\phi_\mu(x)dx = (-1)^{N+1}\int_{J_N} \phi_\mu(x)dx.$$

Now J_N is decomposable into $2^{\mu-\nu}$ intervals, in which $\phi_\mu(x)$ is alternately $+1$ and -1. Hence

$$\int_0^1 \phi_\nu(x)\phi_\mu(x)dx = \sum \int_{J_N} \phi_\nu(x)\phi_\mu(x)dx = 0.$$

4. Gram's determinant for any n functions of the sequence has the value $+1$.

5. $e^x = 0{\cdot}83\lambda_0(x) + 1{\cdot}35\lambda_1(x) + 0{\cdot}57\lambda_2(x) + \ldots$

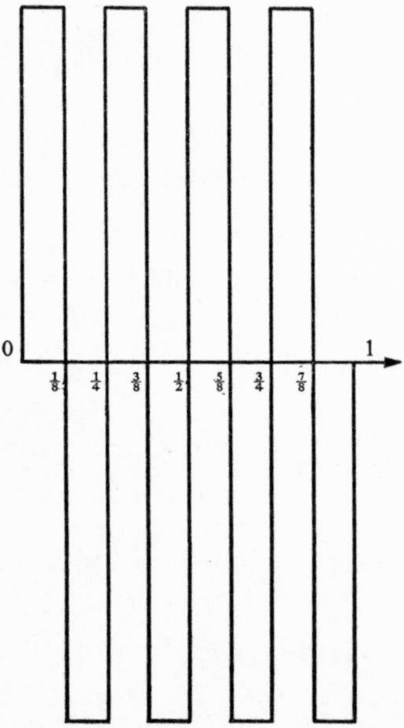

Fig. 15.

6. $$\operatorname{sgn} x = \sum_{m=1}^{\infty} (-1)^m \frac{4m+3}{2m+2} g_m P_{2m+1}(x),$$
where
$$g_m = \frac{1.3.5\ldots(2m-1)}{2.4.6\ldots 2m}.$$

7. By (4.14) if $x_k = \cos(k\pi/n)$, $k = 0, 1, 2, \ldots n$, we have
$$T_n(x_k) = \frac{(-1)^k}{2^{n-1}}.$$

At these points x_k, and at no others, $|T_n(x_k)|$ attains its maximum value. If the relation
$$|\operatorname{Max} p_n(x)| < |\operatorname{Max} T_n(x_k)|$$
were true, then we would have $|p_n(x_k)| < |T_n(x_k)|$ at the points x_k. This would imply that the difference $q_{n-1}(x) = T_n(x) - p_n(x)$ has the following properties:
$$q_{n-1}(x_0) > 0, \qquad q_{n-1}(x_1) < 0,$$
$$q_{n-1}(x_2) > 0, \qquad q_{n-1}(x_3) < 0,$$
$$\cdots\cdots\cdots$$
$$\cdots\cdots\cdots$$
so that the polynomial $q_{n-1}(x)$ would have n zeros. But this is impossible, since $q_{n-1}(x)$ is of degree $n-1$.

CHAPTER V. COMPLETENESS OF SYSTEMS OF FUNCTIONS

1. Start from the inequality
$$(a_2b_1 - a_1b_2)^2 \geqslant 0.$$

2. $$\left(\sum_{\nu=1}^{n} x_\nu \cdot 1\right)^2 \leqslant \sum_{\nu=1}^{n} x_\nu^2 \sum_{\nu=1}^{n} 1^2 = 1 \cdot n.$$

3. $$\| f-\phi \|^2 = ((f-\psi)+(\psi-\phi), (f-\psi)+(\psi-\phi))$$
$$= \| f-\psi \|^2 + \| \psi-\phi \|^2 + (f-\psi, \psi-\phi) + (\psi-\phi, f-\psi).$$

It follows by Schwarz's inequality that

$$\|f-\phi\|^2 \leqslant \|f-\psi\|^2 + \|\psi-\phi\|^2 + 2\|f-\psi\|\,\|\psi-\phi\|. \tag{1}$$

Now $\{\|f-\psi\| - \|\psi-\phi\|\}^2 \geqslant 0$; hence

$$2\|f-\psi\|\,\|\psi-\phi\| \leqq \|f-\psi\|^2 + \|\psi-\phi\|^2.$$

It therefore follows from equation (1) above that

$$\|f-\phi\|^2 \leqslant 2\{\|f-\psi\|^2 + \|\psi-\phi\|^2\}.$$

4. Multiply the identity

$$\sum_{k=0}^{n} \binom{n}{k} x^k(1-x)^{n-k} = 1$$

by $f(x)$ and find an upper bound for the difference $|f(x)-B_n(x)|$.

CHAPTER VI. EIGENVALUE PROBLEMS IN MATHEMATICAL PHYSICS

1. Multiply the equations

$$y_m'' + Ay_m' + \lambda_m y_m = 0$$
$$y_n'' + Ay_n' + \lambda_n y_n = 0$$

by y_n and y_m respectively and subtract. Integration from a to b then gives

$$\int_a^b (\lambda_n - \lambda_m) y_n(x) y_m(x) dx = \int_a^b (y_m'' y_n - y_n'' y_m) dx.$$

Integrating by parts we then have, since $y_m(a) = y_m(b) = y_n(a) = y_n(b) = 0$, and $\lambda_n \neq \lambda_m$,

$$\int_a^b y_n(x) y_m(x) dx = 0.$$

2. By (6.45) we have

$$\frac{1}{\lambda_n}\phi_n(x) = \int_a^b K(x,t)\phi_n(t)dt, \tag{2}$$

and hence the left side of this equation is the Fourier coefficient of the function $K(x,t)$. By Bessel's inequality we then have

$$\sum_{n=1}^{\infty} \frac{1}{\lambda_n^2}\{\phi_n(x)\}^2 \leqslant \int_a^b |K(x,t)|^2 dt = K(x,x). \tag{3}$$

3. The result follows by integration of the relation (3) in the preceding solution.

4. The integral

$$\int_0^1 t\phi(t)dt = c$$

is a constant. Hence $y(x)$ is of the form $1+cx$. Substitution in the integral equation gives $c = \frac{3}{4}$.

5. Let $y(x)$ be a solution of (6.46), and suppose it can be expressed in the form

$$y(x) - f(x) = \sum_{\nu=1}^{\infty} c_\nu \phi_\nu(x);$$

let

$$f(x) = \sum_{\nu=1}^{\infty} b_\nu \phi_\nu(x).$$

Then by (2) in the solution of Exercise 2 above

$$\sum_{\nu=1}^{\infty} c_\nu \phi_\nu(x) = \sum_{\nu=1}^{\infty} b_\nu \phi_\nu(x) + \lambda \sum_{\nu=1}^{\infty} c_\nu \int_a^b K(x,t)\phi_\nu(t)dt$$

$$= \sum_{\nu=1}^{\infty} b_\nu \phi_\nu(x) + \lambda \sum_{\nu=1}^{\infty} \frac{c_\nu}{\lambda_\nu} \phi_\nu(x).$$

Comparing coefficients we obtain

$$c_\nu = b_\nu + \frac{\lambda}{\lambda_\nu} c_\nu,$$

so that

$$y(x) = \sum_{\nu=1}^{\infty} \frac{b_\nu \lambda_\nu}{\lambda_\nu - \lambda} \phi_\nu(x) = f(x) + \sum_{\nu=1}^{\infty} \frac{\lambda b_\nu}{\lambda_\nu - \lambda} \phi_\nu(x).$$

Hence, provided a solution of (6.46) exists, which can be expressed by means of the orthonormal system $\phi_\nu(x)$, it is given by the series (6·47). We see by substitution that (6.47) is actually a solution.

CHAPTER VII. HILBERT SPACES

1. In any interval $[\varepsilon, 1]$, where $0<\varepsilon<1$, only a finite number of the functions $\phi_n(x)$ are non-zero. From this the continuity of all the functions

$$\sum_{n=1}^{\infty} a_n\phi_n(x)$$

follows.

2. In any interval $[-1, 1-\varepsilon]$, where $0<\varepsilon<1$, the functions of the sequence $\psi_n(x)$ are uniformly bounded. From this the continuity of the functions

$$\sum_{n=1}^{\infty} a_n\psi_n(x)$$

follows.

3. We have, for $\lambda \neq \mu$,

$$\lim_{T\to\infty} \frac{1}{2T}\int_{-T}^{T} e^{i(\lambda-\mu)t}dt = \lim_{\tau\to\infty} \frac{e^{i\tau}-e^{-i\tau}}{2i\tau} = \lim_{\tau\to\infty} \frac{\sin\tau}{\tau} = 0.$$

On the other hand when $\lambda = \mu$ we have

$$\lim_{T\to\infty} \frac{1}{2T}\int_{-T}^{T} dt = 1.$$

CHAPTER VIII. THE SOLUTION OF LINEAR SYSTEMS

1. The components $s_k^{(n)}$ of the given vector sequence $s^{(n)}$ satisfy the relation

$$\lim_{n\to\infty} s_k^{(n)} = 0,$$

but $s^{(n)}$ is not a null-sequence. For we have

$$\| s^{(n)} \|^2 = (s^{(n)}, s^{(n)}) = 1 + \frac{1}{2^2} + \frac{1}{3^2} + \ldots,$$

so that

$$\lim_{n \to \infty} \| s^{(n)} - \underline{0} \| \neq 0.$$

2. If a linear relation

$$\beta_0 A^{(0)} + \beta_1 A^{(1)} + \ldots + \beta_r A^{(r)} = 0$$

with $r \geqslant 2$ existed between the rows $A^{(\rho)}$ of the matrix (8.51) we could derive in succession $\beta_r = \beta_{r-1} = \ldots = \beta_2 = 0$. A relation $\beta_0 A^{(0)} + \beta_1 A^{(1)} = \underline{0}$ is possible only if the determinant

$$\begin{vmatrix} \frac{1}{2}\lambda & 1 \\ 1 & \lambda - 1 \end{vmatrix}$$

vanishes.

3. $\| z^{(n)} \|^2 =$

$$\begin{vmatrix} (A^{(1)}, A^{(1)}) \ldots (A^{(1)}, A^{(n)}) & (A^{(1)}, y) \\ \cdot & \\ \cdot & \\ \cdot & \\ (A^{(n)}, A^{(1)}) \ldots (A^{(n)}, A^{(n)}) & (A^{(n)}, y) \\ (y, A^{(1)}) \quad \ldots (y, A^{(n)}) & (y, y) \end{vmatrix} \div \det\{(A^{(i)}, A^{(k)})\}.$$

CHAPTER IX. REPRODUCING KERNELS

1. (a) It follows from the definition of the functions $\psi_n(x)$ that they are uniformly bounded in any interval $(-1, 1-\varepsilon)$. Hence $\sum \{\psi_n(x)\}^2$ is also uniformly bounded, a finite number of terms at most of this series being non-zero, for any given x. By Schwarz's inequality, it follows that all series $\sum a_n \psi_n(x)$ for which $\sum |a_n|^2 < \infty$

converge uniformly. All the functions of the space are therefore continuous, including the kernel function $K(x,t)$.

(b) By the definition of the functions $\psi_n(x)$, $K(0,0) = 0$, but

$$K\left(\tfrac{1}{2}(c_n+c_{n+1}),\ \tfrac{1}{2}(c_n+c_{n+1})\right) = \{\psi_n(\tfrac{1}{2}(c_n+c_{n+1}))\}^2 = 1,$$

where $c_n = 2^{-n}$, so that

$$\overline{\lim_{x\to 0}}\, K(x,x) = 1.$$

2. For separable spaces this result immediately follows from the fact that the kernel function can be expressed in the form (9.1) (cf. Exercise 3 below); for the general case, see Meschkowski (2) p. 47.

3. Let H be separable. The expression for the kernel function in terms of a complete system $\phi_n(x)$,

$$K(x,t) = \sum_{n=1}^{\infty} b_n(t)\phi_n(x),$$

leads to

$$b_n(t) = (K(x,t),\phi_n(x))_x = \overline{\phi_n(t)}.$$

Again, suppose (9.1) holds; then we have, for any element $f(x) \in H$, by (9.2),

$$f(t) = (f(x),K(x,t))_x = \left(f(x), \sum_{n=1}^{\infty} \phi_n(x)\overline{\phi_n(t)}\right)_x$$

$$= \sum_{n=1}^{\infty} (f,\phi_n)\phi_n(t).$$

Every $f \in H$ can be expressed in this way; hence H is separable.

4. The solution is obtained by putting

$$f(x) = \sum_{\nu=1}^{N} \alpha_\nu K(x,\alpha_\nu),$$

where the coefficients α_ν are to be found from the system of equations

$$\sum_{\nu=1}^{N} \alpha_\nu K(a_n,a_\nu) = b_n, \qquad (n = 1,2, \ldots, N).$$

This will be possible, provided the determinant

$$D = \det\{K(a_n,a_\nu)\}$$

does not vanish.

BIBLIOGRAPHY

References to textbooks in the original German edition have in many cases been supplemented or replaced by alternatives more readily accessible to English-speaking readers. References to Professor Meschkowski's own works, as well as to certain standard texts, have been retained.

AITKEN, A. C. *Determinants and Matrices.* Oliver & Boyd, Edinburgh, 1956.

AKHIESER, N. I. *Theory of Approximation.* Ungar, New York, 1956.

BERGMAN, S. *The Kernel Function and Conformal Mapping* (Math. Surveys 5). American Math. Soc., New York, 1950.

BERGMAN S. and SCHIFFER, M. *Kernel Functions and Elliptic Differential Equations in Mathematical Physics.* Academic Press, New York, 1953.

BORN, M. *Atomic Physics.* Blackie, London and Glasgow, 1962.

CARSLAW, H. S. *Introduction to the Theory of Fourier's Series and Integrals.* Macmillan, London, 1930.

COPSON, E. T. *An Introduction to the Theory of Functions of a Complex Variable.* Oxford Univ. Press, 1960.

COURANT, R. and HILBERT, D. *Methods of Mathematical Physics.* Interscience, New York, 1961.

FERRAR, W. L. *Textbook of Convergence.* Oxford Univ. Press, 1951.

GERONIMUS, Y. L. *Polynomials Orthogonal on a Circle and Interval.* Oxford Univ. Press, 1960.

HAMEL, G. *Integralgleichungen: Einführung in Lehre und Gebrauch.* Springer, Berlin, 1949.

HARDY, G. H. and ROGOSINSKI, W. W. *Fourier Series.* Cambridge Univ. Press, 1950.

HYSLOP, J. M. *Infinite Series.* Oliver & Boyd, Edinburgh, 1954.

KACZMARZ, S. and STEINHAUS, H. *Theorie der Orthogonalreihen.* Warsaw, 1935.

KNOPP, K. *Infinite Series.* Blackie, London and Glasgow, 1951.

KOLMOGOROV, A. N. and FOMIN, S. V. *Elements of the Theory of Functions and Functional Analysis*, Vol 2: *Measure, The Lebesgue Integral and Hilbert Space*. Graylock Press, Rochester, N.Y., 1961.

MESCHKOWSKI, H. (1) *Differenzengleichungen* (*Studia mathematica Vol. XIV*). Vandenhoeck & Ruprecht, Göttingen, 1959.

MESCHKOWSKI, H. (2) *Hilbertsche Räume mit Kernfunktion*. Springer, Berlin, 1962.

MESCHKOWSKI, H. (3) *Unendliche Reihen*. Bibliographisches Institut, Mannheim, 1961.

MILNE-THOMSON, L. M. *The Calculus of Finite Differences*. Macmillan, London, 1960.

NATANSON, I. P. *Theory of Functions of a Real Variable*. Ungar, New York, 1960.

NÖRLUND, N. E. *Vorlesungen über Differenzenrechnung*. Springer, Berlin, 1924.

RIESZ, F. and NAGY, B. SZ-. *Functional Analysis*. Blackie, London and Glasgow, 1955.

RUTHERFORD, D. E. *Classical Mechanics*. Oliver & Boyd, Edinburgh, 1964.

SCHIFF, L. I. *Quantum Mechanics*. McGraw-Hill, New York, 1955.

SCHMIDT, E. Über die Auflösung linearer Gleichungen mit unendlich vielen Unbekannten. *Rc. Circ. mat. Palermo*, **25**, (1908), 53-77.

SCHMEIDLER, W. *Integralgleichungen mit Anwendungen in Physik und Technik*. Akademische Verlagsges., Leipzig, 1955.

SCHMEIDLER, W. *Linear Operators in Hilbert Space*. Academic Press, New York and London, 1965.

TRICOMI, F. G. *Vorlesungen über Orthogonalreihen*. Springer, Berlin, 1955.

INDEX